Chick had read *The Adventures of Wonder Pug!*
127 times. Every page was packed with excitement.

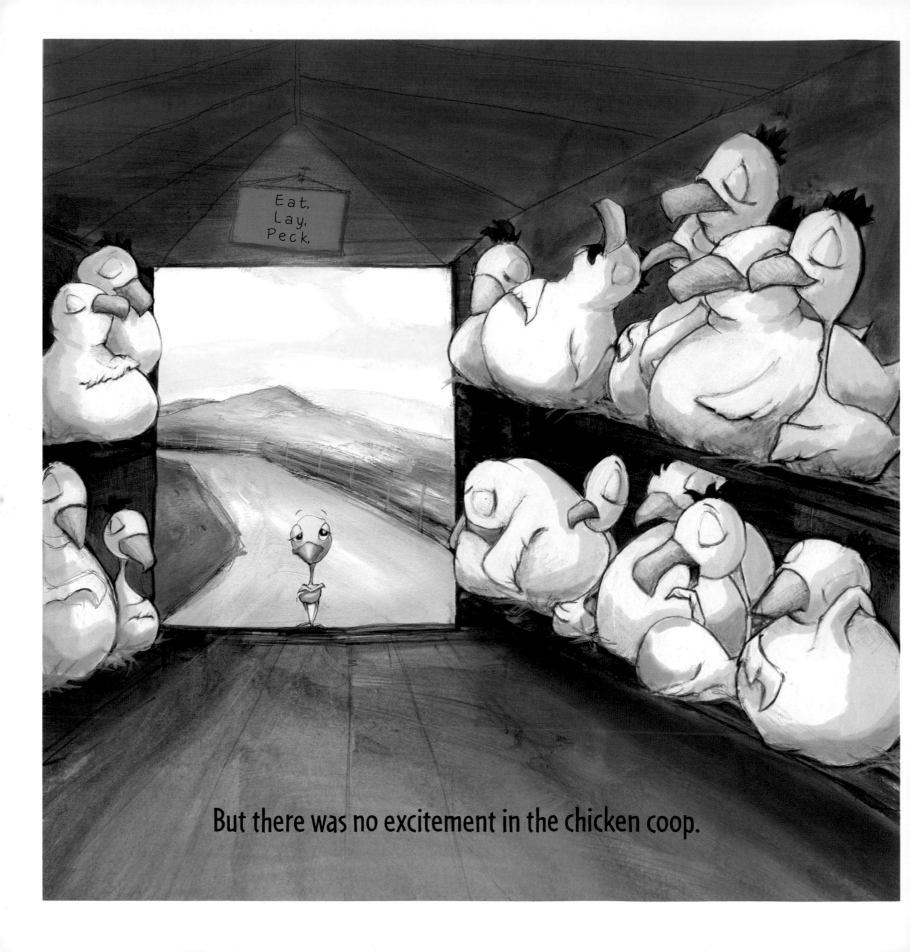

But there was no excitement in the chicken coop.

So Chick set off to find some.

It wasn't long before he found a real-life Wonder Pug.

'Wow.' Chick swooned. Even asleep he looked wonderful.

Chick waited for his hero to wake up.

But sometimes even a hero needs a wake-up call.

'You're Wonder Pug, right?' Chick asked.

'I'm a pug. I **was** a sleeping pug.'

'Well, Pug.' Chick sighed. 'I think you're magnificent.
I'm going to be a Wonder Pug when I grow up.'

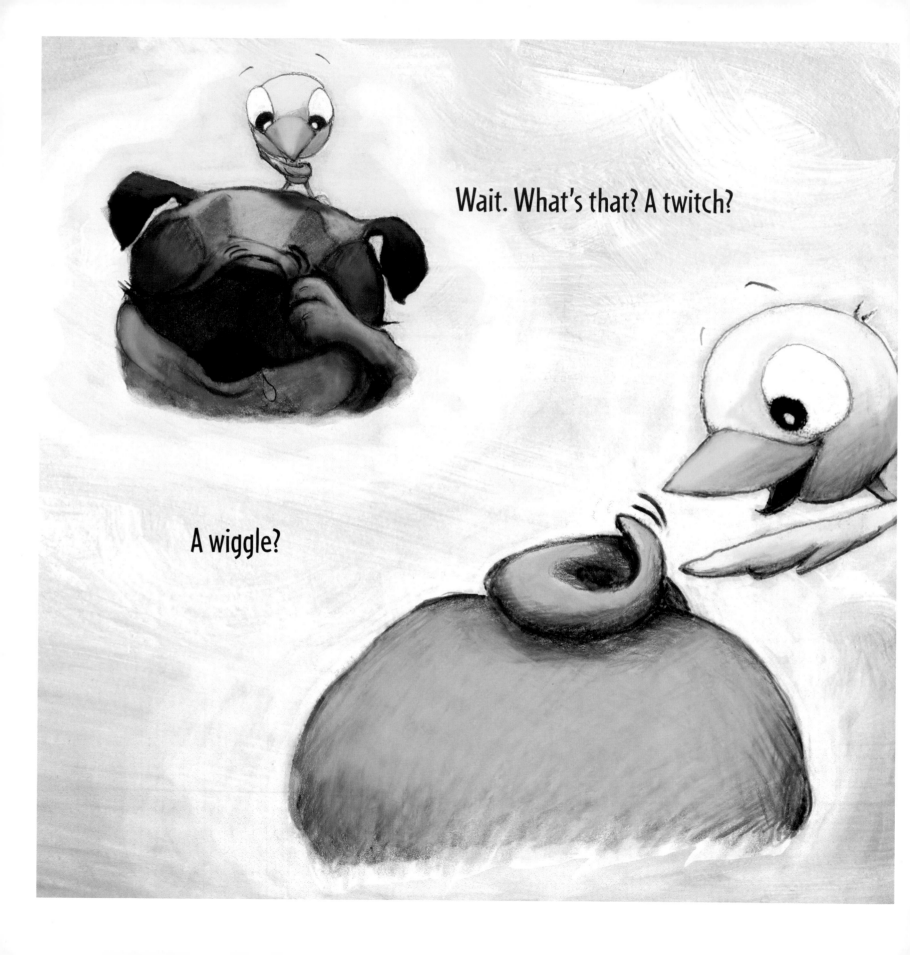

Wait. What's that? A twitch?

A wiggle?

'OK! Here we go!' Chick was all aflutter
with excitement. 'Let the adventure begin!'

'Go get 'em, Tiger! Show that knotted rope who's boss!'

'What about this frisbee? Are you just going to let it taunt you like that?'

'You never know when an empty tin might turn on you.'

'Look at him go! He must have trained vigorously to beat such an opponent!'

Chick was impressed.

Clearly, Pug's strategy was to play dead.

There must be something I can do, thought Chick.

But what? A staring contest?

An egg, right in the kisser?

And then it came to him . . .

Hmmf . . .

'Mr Snuggles didn't count on Wonder Pug having a sidekick, did he?'

external timber cladding

2nd edition

Patrick J Hislop RIBA

TRADA Technology

TRADA Technology Ltd
Chiltern House
Stocking Lane
Hughenden Valley
High Wycombe
Buckinghamshire HP14 4ND

tel: +44 (0)1494 569600
fax: +44 (0)1494 565487
email: information@trada.co.uk
website: www.trada.co.uk

2nd edition 2007

ISBN 978-1-900510-55-4

1st edition published in 2000 by TRADA Technology Ltd.
Whilst every effort is made to ensure the accuracy of the advice given, the company cannot accept liability for loss or damage arising from the information supplied.

This book is printed on paper made from fully managed and sustained forest sources.

TT-COC-002303

© 1996 Forest Stewardship Council A.C.

Printed on paper comprising 50% post consumer 50% pre-consumer waste.

Cover photographs: main, Seton Main house, Paterson Architects. Photo © Keith Hunter Photography
Inset photographs - cover and opposite: left to right
Welney Wetland Centre, Architects: Allies and Morrison. Photo © Allies and Morrison
National Maritime Museum, Long and Kentish Architects. Photo © Long and Kentish Architects
The Core, Eden Project, Grimshaw Architects. Photo © Adam Coupe Photography
Greenwich Millennium School, Edward Cullinen Architects. Photo © ECA

external timber cladding

Timber cladding provides an attractive, lasting and durable external finish and its environmental credentials are leading to increased usage on buildings of all types. However, the performance attributes are only achieved through an understanding of the appropriate design principles and materials selection.

External timber cladding provides guidance to designers and specifiers to enable best practice principles to be applied to external timber cladding. This 2nd edition includes information on materials not covered in the 1st edition, such as wood-based panel products, pre-finished and manufactured products.

A series of **building case studies**, which includes projects featuring timber cladding is available on the TRADA website, www.trada.co.uk. An overview of each project is available to users who register on the site; TRADA members are able to access and download the full studies. It also includes a specification checklist as an *aide-mémoire* for designers.

TRADA Technology offers a unique mix of technical and environmental support to building professionals and timber suppliers who need solutions to problems. The choice of timber species today is often governed not simply by its technical ability to do the job, but also by its environmental credentials.

TRADA Technology is an independent consultancy company providing a wide range of commercial and training services to the timber and construction industries. Prior to 1994 it was wholly owned by TRADA, the Timber Research and Development Association. It is now a member of the TTL Chiltern Group of companies and is TRADA's appointed provider for its Research and Information programmes and for the administration of its membership services.

For on-line technical information, details of consultancy services, training and TRADA membership visit www.trada.co.uk or telephone 01494 569600.

Also within the TTL Chiltern Group is **BM TRADA Certification** a leading multi-sector certification body accredited by UKAS (United Kingdom Accreditation Service). BM TRADA's portfolio of services includes certification to quality, environmental, information security, and health & safety management systems. Its certification services include chain of custody - FSC, PEFC, and Forest Product schemes.

For certification and chain of custody information visit www.bmtrada.com or telephone 01494 569700.

TRADA, the Timber Research and Development Association is a not-for-profit, membership-based organisation delivering key services to members in support of its two main aims of 'Building markets for timber' and 'Increasing specification'. Membership encompasses companies and individuals across the entire timber supply/use chain, from foresters and sawmillers, through merchants and manufacturers, to architects, engineers and specifiers.

For further information and details of membership visit www.trada.co.uk or telephone 01494 569603.

Contents

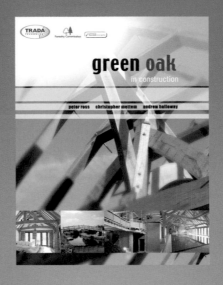
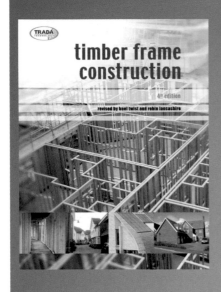

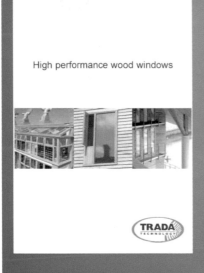

1 Timber for external cladding

Judging by the coverage in the architectural press, there is a growing interest amongst architects in the use of timber for cladding, not only for domestic construction, but also for much larger and more prestigious buildings. This increased interest is not unique to Great Britain; there are also more international examples of innovative uses of timber as cladding. A prime reason for this interest is a recognition of the 'green' qualities of timber as a building material.

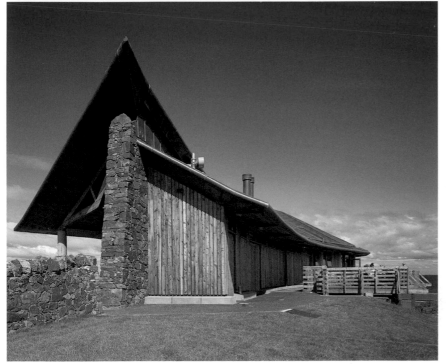

Figure 1.1 top left
Green oak cladding, National Maritime Museum, Cornwall
Long and Kentish Architects
Photo © Long and Kentish Architects

Figure 1.2 above
Stained softwood boarding, Exhibition building, Sutton Hoo, Suffolk
Architects: van Heyningen and Haward
Photo T Hyland

Figure 1.3 left
Scottish Seabird Centre, North Berwick
Architects: Simpson and Brown
Photo © Keith Hudson Photography

Figure 1.4 Coloured stains used on softwood boarding and deck structures in housing
Architects: Architype
Photo © Architype

Converting a log to boards generally uses little energy and produces less toxic pollution to the environment than the production of most other materials. However, the extent of transport, drying, preservative treatment, machining, coating and maintaining any finish to the wood obviously has a proportionate bearing on the total energy consumption required and effects on the environment. Careful selection of species and appropriate specification of finishes can minimise energy use and environmental impact both initially and in the long term use of the building.

Most timber cladding is softwood, which can be readily obtained from the expanding coniferous forests in both the Northern and Southern hemispheres, a huge source of renewable building material. Softwoods such as western red cedar, European larch or Douglas fir may be chosen for cladding because of their inherent durability but less durable woods, such as European redwood or whitewood treated with preservatives, can be equally suitable.

Figure 1.5 Douglas fir cladding on the David Douglas Pavilion, Pitlochry
Gaia Architects
Photo © Robin Baker

Tropical hardwoods are also used for cladding but there is an increasing interest in the use of durable temperate hardwoods, such as European oak or sweet chestnut. European oak has a long tradition of use in the UK, left unfinished and allowed to weather to a natural silver grey in which state it has lasted for many centuries without maintenance. There are now extensive forests of oak all over Europe and an expanding resource in the British Isles, despite the depletion of our major deciduous forests up to the end of the 18th century. Much of this British woodland would benefit from thinning and this could supply much of the wood for the board sizes preferred for cladding. The wood can be used 'green' ie undried, which reduces both the energy required and the cost of drying, but careful detailing is necessary in order to ensure that sufficient allowance is made for drying shrinkage after the boards are erected on the building.

Timber cladding is a 'dry' process which not only reduces construction time but it can be designed to be made up into prefabricated panels, further reducing construction time on site.

The renewed interest in using wood to clad timber buildings has also extended to the use of wood to clad blockwork, concrete or steel framed buildings. Although usually chosen for visual reasons and used as a "rain screen" to the wall behind, there is an additional advantage in that it allows extra insulation to be located outside a masonry wall behind the boarding. This external insulation may provide the full thermal performance of the building or contribute to improving the insulation of existing buildings.

1.1 History of use

Timber has long been used to construct the external walls of buildings, either as the primary form of structure and enclosure or merely to enclose a separate structural frame. Structural timber walling originally consisted of thick boards set directly into the ground to support the roof at the eaves, with a framed wall or post structure to take internal loads. This is referred to as "stave" or "palisade" construction (*Figure 1.7*). Alternatively, the load bearing walls were made of debarked logs merely stacked together and overlapped at the corners. This is the log construction originally found in the Alps, Scandinavia and later, in North America (*Figure 1.8*).

More commonly, non structural timber cladding was used to protect a separate internal frame consisting of large posts directly supporting major roof trusses. Between these trusses, common rafters were supported on purlins and between the posts the cladding was supported on cladding rails or smaller posts. This is typical of early barn construction, particularly in East Anglia, where the posts and wall framing were concealed by the cladding, rather than left exposed as in other parts of the country (*Figure 1.9*). This barn construction was the model for the earliest buildings in New England, where substantial hardwood frames were used until the local deciduous forests were depleted and this wood became scarce and expensive. From this time the more typically modern method of construction became popular using closely spaced small section softwood studs (posts) as load bearing walls to directly support roof rafters and cladding.

Figure 1.6 Reconstruction of typical Anglo Saxon housing, West Stow, Suffolk
Photo P Hislop

Figure 1.7 Stave Church, Norway

Figure 1.8 Alpine log construction

Figure 1.9 The Wheat Barn, Cressing Temple, Essex
Photo © C J Mettem

Figure 1.10 13th century Hansa buildings, Bergen
Photo P Hislop

Figure 1.11 'Falun' coating on timber cladding
Photo P Hislop

Figure 1.12 18th century timber church in New England
Photo P Hislop

Figure 1.13 Traditional Finnish housing
Photo P Hislop

There were two developments that encouraged the use of this form of construction. Originally boards were sawn from the log locally in saw pits operated by two men. The realisation that water power could speed the process and reduce the manual effort required meant that sawmills were built alongside rivers located in the coniferous forests, cutting the timber for stock rather than specifically for individual buildings. This resulted in the introduction of standard size sections for framing, planking and cladding boards. Although split shingles and shakes were still commonly used for cladding, sawn boards became more common, particularly for urban buildings. This became known as "clapboard" construction in North America. The other development was the introduction of the mass produced steel nail, which not only overcame the need for traditional carpentry joints and allowed much smaller sections of timber to be used as framing, but also made timber cladding less expensive. This softwood framed and timber clad construction had already existed for hundreds of years in Scandinavia and there are still buildings of this type that have survived since the 13th century in Norway.

In most parts of the world where this form of timber frame construction has become the standard method of building, the frame buildings are still clad in timber boards, shingles or shakes. These materials frequently last the life of the building, often in fairly extreme climates as well as those comparable with the British Isles. While durable softwoods, such as western red cedar, were historically used as unfinished shingles or boards, less durable softwoods, such as European redwoods and whitewoods, were usually stained or painted. In Sweden, by Royal decree in the 17th Century, all wood clad buildings had to be finished with a coating of "Falun" a mixture of oil, rye and wheat dust with ferrous oxides which, besides resulting in the traditional red colour of Swedish timber buildings, also provided an effective long term protection to the wood, only requiring occasional repainting (*Figure 1.11*).

With the worldwide introduction in the 18th century of the Renaissance, or Classical, style of architecture into countries where timber was the primary building material, the construction was refined to suit the new style. Architectural motifs such as pediments, columns and cornices and quoins made elsewhere from stone or stucco, were copied in wood. Façades were typically painted in white, pastel colours or grey with the decorative motifs in white. This resulted in an elegant domestic style of architecture, originally in New England, but later associated with the Colonial style of the large mansions of the southern United States (*Figure 1.12*).

A more unusual application of wood for cladding in North America was the use of small panels of hardwood to simulate individual blocks of ashlar stone. These panels were hung directly on to the timber framing, and left unfinished to weather naturally. The eventual result was a surprisingly convincing impression of classical stone walling (*Figure 1.14*).

Although examples of timber framed buildings have existed since the 18th century, because of the strong tradition of brick buildings in the UK, most were either faced with plain or "mathematical" clay tiles to simulate brickwork. Some timber frame buildings even had an additional brick skin, or lime render, added later to conceal the original wood cladding in order to raise the "status" of the building.

There are still however many examples of an earlier form of timber cladding existing in the south of England in the old farm buildings which were faced with tarred or creosoted softwood boards, unfinished oak or wide 'waney' edged boards of elm.

Some imported timber frame buildings were erected in the British Isles in the 1930's and these were generally clad with unfinished cedar boards or shingles. These have generally lasted well with little physical deterioration, but in some cases the buildings have been subsequently coated with unsuitable paints. These finishes either trapped moisture in the wood, causing decay, or were not maintained adequately which resulted in a poor overall appearance. Correctly designed rainscreen cladding and modern stains or paint will avoid such problems.

Timber cladding provides an attractive, economic and environmentally friendly way for designers and specifiers to enclose buildings. As construction in the UK changes to embrace the concepts of sustainable development and increased prefabrication, the popularity of timber cladding is set to rise even further.

Figure 1.14 Hardwood panels simulating ashlar stone. 18th century, New England
Photo P Hislop

2 Types of cladding

Timber cladding can be used in many forms in order to produce a wide variety of pattern, texture and colour. This range can extend from shingles, shakes and logs, through to close boarded panels. However, the most common forms of timber cladding consist of boards laid either vertically, diagonally or horizontally with overlapping or flush faces. If one adds to this the possible variations in board width, surface finish, profile shape, joint design, the use of virtually unlimited range of colours, or the texture and character of each species left unfinished, the versatility of timber cladding becomes apparent.

When choosing any particular form of board cladding, the choice of species, the size and length of boards available, the degree of weather protection, the ease of erection, the method of fixing, the choice of finish and the robustness of the material should all be amongst the many aspects to be considered. This is necessary in order to ensure that the completed wall achieves the required performance, the expected durability with minimum maintenance, and the visual effect required within acceptable costs.

Boarding can be used vertically, diagonally or horizontally and this is probably the first choice that needs to be made when considering the visual aspects. Before describing the advantages and limitations of each, there are some general aspects of design that apply to all three types.

Although some standard cladding profiles have been available commercially for many years and are included in *BS 1186-3 Timber for and workmanship in joinery. Wood trim*, they may be more suitable for internal use rather than external. The profiles included in *BS EN 15146 Solid softwood panelling and cladding. Machined profiles without tongue and groove* are equally more suitable for internal use than external.

Special profiles of board can generally be machined to order, if a reasonable quantity is required. It is important that designers fully understand the principles of weatherproof design, allow for the likely movement of the wood due to variation in moisture content, and understand the practicality of obtaining the required lengths and widths in the species chosen. The ease of machining, the strength of the sections during handling and installation and any particular problems of erecting the cladding on the building should also be considered as these will have a bearing on the practicality of the type of cladding chosen as well as the final cost. On larger, repetitive, or high level installations, there may be considerable advantage, for instance, in designing for as much prefabrication as possible. It may be sensible therefore to discuss these aspects with both timber suppliers and installation contractors before finalising the design.

2.1 Horizontal boards

Horizontal layouts are probably the most common type of board cladding. They can be nailed to vertical battens on either timber frame or masonry walls. The boards can be used in a simple overlap design, feather or square edged, or as rebated feather edge or shiplap where a more flush surface is required. Tongued and grooved boards can also be used but are better with a rebated profile and a limited face width.

Figure 2.1 Horizontal larch weatherboarding, Welney Wetland Centre. Architects: Allies and Morrison
Photo © Allies and Morrison

Figure 2.2 National Memorial Arboretum Architects: Architype
Photo © Architype

Figure 2.3 Siberian larch cladding, Holly Barn, Norfolk
Knox Bhavan Architects
Photo © Dennis Gilbert / VIEW

Horizontal boards can also be used in an 'open jointed' form with the top and bottom edges of the board chamfered, rather than square-cut, to drain water to the outside and provide some overlap. The open gap between the boards will give a strong shadow line which is visually useful if the boards are used "green" as shrinkage and minor distortion of the boards can be somewhat unpredictable and the heavy shadow line conceals these variations. If open jointed boards are to be used the potential effect of u/v light reaching a breather membrane behind should be taken into account, see Section 5.4.1.

When designing the layout of horizontal cladding, it is necessary to consider how the boards will be jointed end to end. Because extra battens may be necessary at butt joints between the ends of boards to provide adequate width for fixing, it may be preferable to standardise the lengths of the boards rather than use random lengths. In this case all end joints can occur in line, on double battens, giving a "panellised" effect to the wall. "Panellising" will also make it easier to prefabricate the panels. If a more monolithic appearance is required, "random" board lengths should be used but these should be in multiples of the batten spacing. In this case, an additional short length of batten can be nailed to the side of the existing batten to provide the extra width required at end joints for the fixings, see Section 5.3.

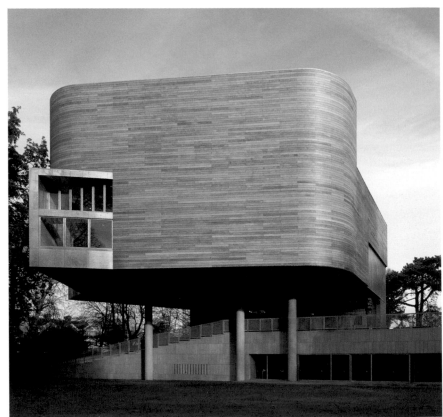

Figure 2.4 Lewis Glucksman gallery, University College, Cork
Architects: O'Donnell + Tuomey
Photo © Dennis Gilbert / VIEW

2.2 Diagonal boards

In a diagonal layout the boards are usually angled at 45° and fixed to vertical battens coincident with timber studs or battens fixed directly to masonry walls. Used diagonally, the board has to span further than if used horizontally or vertically and it may be necessary to use a thicker board or to close up the centres of the battens behind. Battens can also be arranged diagonally to reduce the board span which allows any water that penetrates the boarding to run down the battens. It may not be necessary to use counter battens if there is sufficient gap for ventilation and drainage at the base of the wall and at the ends of the battens. It is advisable not to run the boards into a V-pattern because of the volume of water that will collect at the junction. If a "chevron" effect is required the boards should drain away from any vertical joints between the ends of the boards rather than towards them. Simple overlap board designs are not suitable for diagonal use and it is not advisable to use an open-joint design as there will be considerable rainwater penetration. Butt-joints between the ends of boards will also be liable to leakage, so in a diagonal pattern longer boards are generally necessary to avoid butt-joints on the length.

Figure 2.5 Diagonal cladding, Wood Research Centre, Honduras
Architects:TRADA

15

2.3 Vertical boards

Tongued and grooved boards are frequently used for vertical cladding but the board widths should be limited to ensure that moisture movement does not result in disengagement of the tongues. An alternative is to use a rebated board that provides a flush surface but which has sufficient overlap to allow for possible shrinkage. Vertical boards with open joints on battens can be used but more rainwater will be driven through the joints than with open jointed horizontal boards. The potential effect of u/v light on the durability of a breather membrane in the cavity behind should be checked with the membrane manufacturer if open joints are to be used, particularly as more daylight may penetrate than with open jointed horizontal boards.

Figure 2.6 Vertical boarding, Orchard Building, Bedales School, Hampshire. Architects: Walters and Cohen Photos © Walters and Cohen/ Wood Awards

Figure 2.7 Board-on-board cladding, Co-housing, Stroud
Architects: Architype
Photo © Leigh Simpson

Figure 2.8 Vertical boarding, Findhorn Centre
Photo P Hislop

Figure 2.9 Board on board cladding, Student accommodation, Germany
Architects: Peter Hubner

Figure 2.10 University of Limerick
Project Architects
Photo T Hyland

The simplest form of vertical cladding is "board-on-board". This consists of an inner layer of boards spaced apart over which a layer of outer boards is fixed to cover the gaps between the inner boards. A great range of surface modelling can be achieved by varying the widths of the boards or battens in each layer. This cladding can be done with simple rectangular boards or the outer layer boards may be of a different profile to accentuate the modelling of the surface. A board-on-board layout is very tolerant of dimensional variation. It is also particularly well suited to accommodating curves in plan but the use of narrow boards is preferable if the curve is of a tight radius. Sufficient overlap must always be provided to allow for any shrinkage of the boards. A further advantage of board-on-board is that the gap between the outer board and the horizontal fixing battens will provide sufficient ventilation and drainage to the cavity behind without the need for counter battens.

If boards are to be used vertically, the available lengths should be considered, because it is not always easy to ensure that boards are neatly jointed end to end and there is always the risk of swelling in the lower board if rain gets into the end grain of the wood. On multi-storey buildings it is preferable to limit the boards to storey-height lengths and introduce a horizontal flashing at floor level. This may make the cladding easier to prefabricate, close the cavity at floor level if necessary to prevent the vertical spread of fire, and allow for any "creep" or settlement of the building structure.

Figure 2.11 Balfron House
Architects: StudioKAP
Photo © Keith Hunter Photography

2.4 Shingles and shakes

Some of the oldest wood buildings in existence are clad with shingles or shakes. These are tapered pieces of wood in the form of shingles, sawn on both faces, or shakes, traditionally split from the solid wood. They are fixed in overlapping form as a roof or wall cladding finish in a similar manner to slates or plain tiles. On walls, they shed water readily and have proved very durable whether of hardwood, such as oak or sweet chestnut, or softwood, such as western red cedar or European larch.

Although regarded as a very traditional form of cladding, there are now many examples of modern applications. The major attraction of the material is that it is relatively easy to accommodate quite tight curves in plan or section, and sometimes both together.

Figure 2.12 Cedar House
Hudson Architects
Photo © Hudson Architects

In Canada and North America shingles and shakes have traditionally been used for cladding and are normally of western red cedar (or in the west, Californian redwood). They have also been used for roofing on low pitched roofs, and because these do not drain as readily, the service life of shingles has sometimes been compromised. Consequently, virtually all western red cedar shingles imported into Europe, whether for roofing or cladding, are treated with preservative to enhance their durability. It is still possible, but not very common, to obtain shingles or shakes from UK woods such as European oak, sweet chestnut or European larch which are not usually treated with preservative.

Imported shingles from North America generally come in three lengths; 405 mm, 455 mm, and 610 mm, and for vertical cladding not more than 40% of the shingle should be exposed. Similar sizes are available from European suppliers. Individual shingles may vary considerably in width and can be fixed to give a random appearance to the wall.

Shingles or shakes normally span across three horizontal battens and are fixed with stainless steel annular ring shank nails to one batten. The overlapping layer is then nailed through the one below to the next batten up. For

Figure 2.13 left and above
Cedar shingle clad curved wall/roof,
Taplow Court, Berkshire
Architects: Architype
Photos © Architype

Figure 2.14 Chesa Futura apartments, St Moritz
Architects: Foster and Partners
Photo © Nigel Young / Foster + Partners

walls that are curved in section, it is preferable to use the shorter lengths of shingle or shake, with more closely spaced battens, to adapt more easily to a curved surface. It is possible to bend shingles into a curved form by boiling, but this may not be economically viable.

Although it is possible to continue the shingles around external corners by mitreing and lacing, it is simpler to use vertical corner boards for both internal and external corners.

With shakes or shingles it is particularly important to ensure that there is a well ventilated cavity behind to prevent a high moisture content building up in the wood as three layers overlap for part of their length. This form of cladding should still be treated as a rainscreen in that some water may penetrate into the cavity and will need to be drained and ventilated away and there must be a weatherproof wall or membrane behind. Although some air may penetrate between the shingles, it is preferable to add vertical counter battens to provide a clear path for ventilation which would otherwise be blocked by the horizontal battens.

It is not necessary to coat shingles or shakes to achieve the required durability, and in Europe they are usually left to bleach, although stains and paints are frequently applied to shingles in North America. Unfinished shingles may darken with time to varying shades of brown.

Figure 2.15 Cedar shingles. Entrance building, Eden Project, Cornwall.
Grimshaw Architects
Photo © Adam Coupe Photography

2.5 Panel cladding

Plywood panels are frequently used for cladding temporary buildings, but also occasionally for more permanent buildings. They are also often fitted into window frames or curtain walls where the wall needs to be opaque rather than glazed. However, the use of plywood in external conditions, requires considerable care in the detailing. It is obviously necessary to specify an external quality plywood manufactured with suitable glues eg Class 3 to *BS EN 314-2* and to ensure that the veneers are either of a Class 2 (durable) or Class 3 (moderately durable) wood, or pressure treated with preservative.

Figure 2.16 Plywood cladding on TRADA office building, Buckinghamshire, constructed in 1978 Architects: TRADA

Marine plywood is often specified in an effort to ensure that hardwood veneers are adequately durable, but this is expensive and the natural colour may not be acceptable for overcoating. Marine plywood veneers are only required to be Class 3 (moderately durable) and their use will not necessarily prevent the end grain swelling, leading to splitting of the veneers and delamination if the edges are exposed to sustained moisture. It is generally more economic to use pressure treated softwood sheathing plywood which has the same quality gluelines and ensure that there is no risk of moisture being trapped in the end grain of the veneers. It is preferable in this case if the plywood sheets are cut down to the size of the panels to be used before they are treated to ensure good preservative penetration into the edges of the sheets.

The edges of plywood sheets can be protected by commercially available edge sealers or by lipping with treated softwood or hardwood to prevent moisture being absorbed into the end grain of the veneers. Plywood panels should preferably not be 'glazed' into framing members like sheets of glass, because there is a high risk of moisture eventually getting past the beads and possibly accumulating at the bottom of the panel. If a solid infill panel in a glazed wall is required, a minimum 6 mm gap should be left between the edges of the plywood and the framing for ventilation, possible drainage and moisture movement of the panels. Seals should be limited to the inner and outer faces of the panels leaving a drained and ventilated cavity without any bedding between the edges of the plywood and frame. At the bottom it is preferable if a glazing bead is omitted in order to allow the maximum ventilation and drainage, or if a bead is required it is better to use a drained aluminium bead, typical of those designed for insulated glass units.

If plywood panels are to be used without a visible framework, and directly fixed back to studs or battens, the boards should be gapped at vertical joints by at least 6 mm and the gap left unfilled. The edges of the plywood sheet should be sealed, or lipped to prevent water absorption. The top of the sheets must be protected, and the bottom stopped short of any sill or flashing by at least 12 mm.

The disadvantage of this arrangement is that all the fixings will be visible. A feature can be made of screw fixings with washers, but the washers need to have rubber inserts behind to ensure that they are watertight, particularly as it is advisable to drill oversize holes for the screws to allow for moisture movement of the sheets.

A simpler, more reliable, and probably more economic method is to add cover battens of treated softwood or hardwood over the vertical joints between panels. The vertical joint between the panels should still be left open but the panels have the edges sealed with an edge sealer, although a lipping would not normally be necessary. The plywood sheets can be nailed or screwed to the supports, and the fixings concealed behind cover battens across the top as well as the vertical joints (*Figure 2.17*). Machining substantial grooves on the inner face of the cover battens prevents capillary action, draining water behind the batten and also provides pressure relief, preventing rainwater being blown back into the vertical joints. These battens should be nailed or screwed to the support members behind through the gap between the sheets. Any horizontal joints between sheets may require continuous metal flashings to protect the top of the sheet below, by shedding any run-off from the upper sheets.

Plywood cladding must be treated as a 'rain screen' in front of a ventilated and drained cavity to ensure that any water that penetrates into the cavity can be drained away and to ensure that there is sufficient ventilation. This will keep the moisture content on the inner and outer faces of the panels reasonably consistent, reducing any tendency for the sheets to warp.

Another reason for providing a ventilated cavity is that plywood sheets have quite a high vapour resistance compared to wood boarding, This increases with the thickness of the sheet because of the additional gluelines. The ventilated cavity prevents condensation forming on the inner face and will allow any internally generated vapour to diffuse away from behind the plywood.

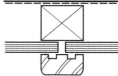

Figure 2.17 Cover batten over vertical joint in plywood cladding

21

Plywood sheets must be thick enough to span between the supports without deflecting under wind load. If 1200 mm wide sheets are used they will require centre fixings unless sufficiently thick plywood is used. With exposed fixings generally intermediate fixings may be visually acceptable, but if battens are concealing the fixings at the vertical joints it may appear inconsistent to expose the fixings in the centre of the panel. If panels are reduced to 600 mm width, intermediate fixings are not necessary and a cover batten will conceal all the fixings. Alternatively, the sheets can be left at their 1200 mm dimensions, but an additional vertical cover batten can be located in the centre of the panel, fixed through to a support batten behind. This stiffens the panel adequately even if relatively thin sheets are used. Horizontal battens directly behind the plywood sheets should be avoided, as they will block the vertical circulation of air behind.

If plywood is to be left exposed, care must be taken to specify an appropriate visual grade, as some softwood sheathing plywood is only sanded on one face, and holes may be patched with plastic inserts. Hardwood plywood may provide a less textured, more consistent appearance, but hardwoods such as birch and some tropical hardwoods are not durable and will need pre-treating with a suitable preservative.

An alternative to relying on the natural appearance of commercially produced plywood sheets is to apply an additional face veneer of better visual quality. This is occasionally used to conceal the lippings around the edges of the panels, but can be vulnerable to damage and may be better limited to panels for internal use only. Cover battens will provide adequate protection to any additional face veneers. On thicker sheets of plywood an additional veneer is unlikely to cause bowing of the sheet but on thin sheets, it may be necessary to add a 'balancing' veneer on the opposite face.

All face veneers on plywood will be liable to surface checking (small cracks) due to exposure. This will not affect the durability of the sheets and may not be very visible, unless a film-forming coating system is used, when the cracks will show up as gaps in the finished film. There is also a risk that the film finish will break down. For this reason, low-build penetrating finishes or high solids coating systems are preferred for plywood as they will colour the wood to the depth of the top veneer concealing the checking and will not break down if surface cracking occurs. Preferably a penetrating stain should be used over a high build coating. Any finish should be sufficiently vapour permeable to avoid moisture being trapped behind the finish.

Pre-finished resin-coated plywood panels have occasionally been used as cladding. These sheets are intended to be used for concrete formwork where the coating can considerably extend the service life of the plywood. They are available in a limited range of colours, but there is no guarantee from the manufacturers that these will not fade over time when exposed to ultRA-ViOLet light. The other major problem is that cutting the panels down to smaller sizes breaks the continuity of the resin-coating protecting the edges of the plywood and some form of additional sealing would be necessary on the cut edges.. Similarly any fixings through the face of the panel become potential points of water ingress.

A possible alternative to conventional plywood for cladding is laminated veneer lumber (LVL). This can be made of softwood or birch veneers, thicker than plywood veneers and produced in thicker panels than plywood. However, because the majority of the veneers run the same way, there is little exposed end grain on the long edges, reducing the risk of moisture absorption on these edges when used vertically. However, similar care must be taken on the top and bottom edges as with plywood. As neither the softwood or the birch veneers are considered durable, pre-treatment with suitable preservative would be advisable.

In the past, GRP encapsulated plywood panels were popular, but could deteriorate internally if there was any breakdown of the GRP casing which allowed moisture to enter the plywood core.

There are plywood panels, generally imported from North America, that are grooved to simulate boarding and sandblasted to imitate a sawn finish. They are generally factory-finished with coloured opaque stains. Where the grooving is deep into the plywood, the end grain of the veneers is exposed and there is a possible risk of moisture absorption unless the end grain is sealed.

A number of sheet materials other than plywood, such as moisture resistant MDF, oil tempered hardboard, OSB etc have been used as cladding panels, but more often on either temporary buildings or relative 'short life' applications such as shop fronts. If these materials are to be used, the manufacturer should be consulted about the particular application, and may be able to offer evidence to cover its suitability for use externally, such as independent third party certification.

2.6 Prefinished, modified and manufactured panels

There are now many panel systems offered commercially, using wood fibre or cellulose based products, which are frequently supported on patented metal grids. A number of these consist of highly compressed wood fibre, or kraft paper layers, which have coloured resin faces or natural wood veneers bonded to the core during the compression process.

Figure 2.18 Prefinished high density wood-faced panels available in a variety of colours
Photos © Prodema SA

These panels come in a range of sizes, but can also be cut down to other sizes and shapes. As there is no end grain exposed to absorb moisture on cut edges, there is less risk of deterioration than with plywood-based panels. There is also less risk of delamination of face veneers because these are bonded to the substrate as part of the manufacturing process. The face veneers are usually durable, stable tropical hardwoods with the additional protection of a factory-applied lacquer finish. The panels are often lipped in matching hardwood.

This type of panel can either be fixed with exposed screws to wooden battens, or hung onto an aluminium support system by clips screwed to the backs of the panels. If direct screw fixings are to be used it is important to allow for some moisture movement that will occur in the panel, and also to ensure that any screw holes are tightly sealed by washers or plastic screw caps.

Another comparatively new product on the market is bamboo plywood, consisting of a tightly compressed core of bamboo fibres, with bamboo veneers on either face and a protective lacquer. The fibres are so tightly packed that it is claimed that there is little end-grain absorption if the boards are cut, but the bamboo needs to be pre-treated with preservative if used externally, as it is not inherently durable.

There has so far been little experience in using this material as external cladding in Europe, so that its suitability for this sort of use has not yet been proved. It would be advisable to generally comply with the recommendations for fixing plywood panels in Section 2.5 if used in this form.

Another development is the use of an aluminium support system onto which small hardwood panels are hung with 'open' vertical and horizontal joints. The support system has been used for some time for terracotta or masonry panels, but has only recently been used for wood panels. A range of very dense, durable and stable tropical woods is offered, all of which have FSC certification. The strongly rectangular visual effect probably suits larger buildings more than small scale domestic buildings. It is an interesting variant on the historical practice of fixing small shaped panels of hardwood

Figure 2.19 Small hardwood panels supported on an aluminium support system. Herriott-Watt University Photo © James and Taylor

onto timber frame construction in order to simulate ashlar stone walls. Like any other timber cladding it requires a ventilated cavity behind, and care has to be taken in the fixing clips and supports to allow for both the thermal movement of the aluminium and the moisture movement of the wood.

There are now various board profiles on the market made from natural wood fibres mixed into resins and extruded (or 'pultruded') through moulds. These are claimed to be more durable, more stable, and stronger than solid timber, but up to now have largely been used for decking rather than cladding.

All these products are promoted by their manufacturers as 'systems' and because there is still little general experience of their use, it is important to obtain sufficient technical information and evidence from the suppliers, preferably via third party accreditation, for the application and use intended. It is also important to obtain information from the manufacturers on planned maintenance requirements for their products and coatings.

2.7 Louvres and brise soleil

With an increased interest in saving energy and using daylight, as opposed to artificial lighting, there is a general trend to increase the size of windows or even to move to totally glazed facades. The disadvantage of this can be excessive glare and possible overheating through large areas of glass in the summer. To counteract these problems, louvres or horizontally projecting 'brise soleil' are now frequently becoming an integral part of facade design.

Louvres are often of timber, either independent components, but sometimes part of the design of timber cladding. In some cases alternate boards or battens are carried across window openings to provide shade, or additional security. In others the whole elevation may be made up of open jointed battens or boards which continue over both solid wall and glazed openings. There are also examples where a shaped horizontal louvre section, designed to shield glazed areas, continues across solid areas of wall as an open jointed cladding system.

If these battens or louvres are of timber, it is important to ensure that the strength and the stiffness of the members is sufficient for the long unsupported spans that may be necessary. It is rarely possible to fix them back to the wall structure at 600 mm or less, which would be normal for cladding boards. They may also be more subject to dynamic wind loading, particularly if they are angled at a low pitch. Self weight can also cause deflection if they are laid horizontally rather than vertically on edge. Flat horizontal louvres are often chosen but, besides the risk of deflection due to self weight, and uplift due to wind, they may also not shed water quickly enough to avoid surface staining due to water tracking back on the underside. It is always advisable to angle the louvres sufficiently steeply to shed water quickly, and the steeper the angle the more structurally efficient the section will be in spanning between the supports.

Figure 2.20 Narrow horizontal boards carried across windows to create louvres. Ski Museum, Lahti, Finland
Photo T Hyland

To minimise penetration of the sun, narrow battens need to be closely spaced vertically, whereas wider boards can be at increased spacing. In this context, if the louvres are to be left unfinished, angled wider boards will shade and protect from rainfall part of the louvre below which may not therefore bleach in the same way as the outer edges of the louvre board.

Figure 2.21 Louvred windows
West London Academy
Architects: Foster and Partners
Photo © Nigel Young / Foster + Partners

Figure 2.22 Iroko louvres protect gable
window at Holly Barn, Norfolk
Knox Bhavan Architects.
Photo © Dennis Gilbert / VIEW

Generally it is advisable to use a strong stiff species for the louvres, particularly if they are spanning some distance. European larch or Douglas fir may therefore be more suitable than western red cedar because of the extra strength, although the western red cedar has the advantage of less self-weight if the louvre is to be used at a very low pitch. If louvres, whether vertical or horizontal, are fixed back at wide centres, there is a risk of distortion of the profiles between the supports. In this case, a denser tropical hardwood may be the best choice because of its strength, stiffness, and limited moisture movement. Any species chosen should be durable, moderately durable or preservatively treated, particularly if to be left unfinished.

A frequent problem in louvre design is ensuring that there is sufficient strength in the fixings to the supports, whether these are steel, aluminium, or timber, because of the stresses generated by wind loading. Sometimes single screw fixings are shown into the back of the louvre section, but with low density material, such as western red cedar or heat-treated timbers, these will quickly work loose. Although hardwoods provide more resistance to pull-out, single fixings generally do not provide sufficient restraint to twisting or possible distortion of the wood.

Timber louvres are often designed to be supported directly off metal sections, usually galvanised steel. A disadvantage of this is that stainless steel screws or bolts, preferable for fixing the timber louvres, are not compatible with mild steel because of the risk of electrolytic action. This is most serious with self drilling fixings, where the galvanising or coating is penetrated and the resulting swarf can corrode in the presence of tannin, causing significant staining of the wood.

It is always preferable to fix the louvres with stainless steel screws to wood frames or battens which may then in turn be fixed to steel structural members using galvanised bolts or screws.

A more robust method of supporting louvres is to form panels of prefabricated timber frames onto which the louvres can be fixed. The best way to support the louvres is then to notch the vertical members to allow part of the louvre to be inserted into the notches and glued as well as screwed, in position. The advantage of this is that the notches will prevent distortion of the louvre, and it may be possible to add intermediate verticals to reduce the span of the louvres. The overall panel can then be fixed back to the secondary structure at relatively wide spacing, suited to the spacing of the vertical wall supports or structural columns.

In some cases horizontal brise soleils may form access walkways for window cleaning or maintenance, in which case the size and span of the wooden louvres and supporting framework must allow for the expected loading and both the louvres and supports should be designed by a structural engineer.

Figure 2.24 Louvred cladding and louvres, Opus One Building, Anglia Ruskin University, Cambridge
Architects: Hawkins/Brown
Photos T Hyland

27

3 Timber selection and quality

3.1 Environmental and certification aspects

Timber is generally regarded as the most environmentally acceptable building material because of its sustainability and energy saving qualities. However, further ecological benefits can be achieved in its selection and use. These include careful choice of species, considering the aspects of transport and production, and using the wood in the most economical manner, including possible recycling

Obtaining adequate assurance of its sustainability through accepted certification organisations is obviously a priority. There are two key elements to ensuring that a timber product derives from well-managed sources. Firstly the forest of origin has to be independently certified to verify that it is being managed in accordance with the requirements of an accredited forest management standard. Secondly, when the timber leaves the forest, it enters a 'chain of custody' system which provides independent certification of its unbroken path from the forest to the consumer, including all stages of manufacturing, transportation and distribution.

The main two schemes for chain of custody certification in the U.K are the Forest Stewardship Council (FSC) and the Programme for the Endorsement of Forest Certification (PEFC). These are both international schemes. Other schemes are nationally-based and their certification logos may be seen on imported timber and timber products.

The government set up the Central Point of Expertise on Timber Procurement (CPET) in 2003 to develop its sustainable timber procurement policy and to provide ongoing advice and guidance to government on sustainability issues. The Government's policy is not only a major influence on the public sector but also within the increasing demands of the private sector. CPET has undertaken several reviews of the major certification schemes on behalf of the Government and announced in December 2006 those schemes which they approved as legal and sustainable. These were:

- Canadian Standards Association (CSA)
- Forest Stewardship Council
- Programme for the Endorsement of Forest Certification
- Sustainable Forestry Initiative (SFI (USA))

The Malaysian Timber Certification Council (MTCC) was classed as meeting the requirements for 'legal sources' only.

Further information is given in the TRADA Wood Information Sheet *Sustainable timber sourcing*.

There is less information available on the other factors influencing the choice of species, such as the energy involved in transport, manufacture, erection, and maintenance, the efficient use of the resource, and even eventual recycling or disposal. However, it is obvious that the use of home-grown wood will reduce the energy required in transport; using naturally durable wood will eliminate the need for preservative treatment; simple

Figure 3.1 Pine forest in the UK
Photo © Adam Coupe Photography

Figure 3.2 Mixed deciduous forest in the UK
Photo © Adam Coupe Photography

sawn profiles will require less energy in production than profiled; unfinished wood will avoid the energy use and by-products of painting; and untreated wood can be disposed of more easily than if it has been treated with preservative. However, choice based purely on any of these features may be over-simplistic and must be weighed against desired performance, service life, appearance and, of course, cost.

3.2 Choice of species

Bearing in mind the general principles outlined above, the actual choice of timber species for cladding on a project must be based primarily on its ability to achieve the desired performance.

Durability is probably the most important consideration in the choice of timber for cladding, and this can be achieved either by the use of preservative treatment, relying on the natural durability of various species or using timber that has been modified in some way to extend its durability.

3.2.1 Natural durability

Five classifications of natural durability are recognised. These relate to the resistance of the heartwood to attack by wood-decaying fungi:

- Class 1 Very durable
- Class 2 Durable
- Class 3 Moderately durable
- Class 4 Slightly durable
- Class 5 Not durable.

Information on durability is given in *BS EN 350 Durability of wood and wood-based products. Natural durability of solid wood. Parts 1 and 2.*

It should be noted that the traditional method of measuring the durability of each species was by embedding a 50 mm x 50 mm stake into the ground. At regular intervals the projecting stake was hit with a sledgehammer, and if it broke it had reached the limit of its life, the durability rating being determined by the number of years it survived. This was an extremely stringent test in that the stake was in full contact with rainwater, snow, insects and soil for the period of the test, representing a far more stringent condition for wood than likely to be experienced on a building, particularly as cladding on a vertical surface and out of ground contact.

For cladding, timbers rated as Class 3, moderately durable or better can be used without preservative treatment, but the non-durable sapwood should be excluded. Timbers rated as Class 4, slightly durable or Class 5, not durable should be pre-treated with preservative, see Section 4.1.

3.2.2 Movement and other properties

The 'movement' properties of timber are also important when selecting species for cladding, particularly for close boarded types. Movement, the dimensional change across the width and thickness of boards, occurs when the moisture content of timber changes in response to a change in atmospheric conditions. It is a relative term and species are classed as small, medium or large movement timbers.

Figure 3.3 This softwood cladding coated with a stain finish after installation shows the effect of subsequent moisture movement

A useful 'rule of thumb' is that within the moisture content range of 5–30% the across grain dimension of timber changes by:

- 1% for every 3% change in moisture content in 'large movement' species
- 1% for every 4% change in moisture content in 'medium movement' species
- 1% for every 5% change in moisture content in 'small movement' species.

However, it is important to note that not all timbers fit neatly within these categories.

Large movement timbers are not generally recommended for use as cladding.

Other properties such as density and hardness can also influence the choice of species although appearance considerations are often determining factors. These and other considerations are discussed below.

3.2.3 Softwoods

The most common choice for cladding is softwood and there are a number of different species suitable. Those widely used include European redwood, European whitewood, European larch, Douglas fir and western red cedar. These, together with other less common timbers, are listed in Appendix 1 with their properties. Further information is available in the TRADA Wood Information Sheets, *Timbers – their properties and uses* and *Wood decorative and practical*.

The coniferous forests of Europe and North America are expanding due to replanting, and virtually all softwoods are now available with FSC or PEFC or North American certification. Home-grown timber is now becoming readily available and includes western red cedar and Douglas fir as well as native species such as spruce (European whitewood), Scots pine (European redwood), and European larch. UK grown softwoods largely come from forests under the Forestry Commission which ensures compliance with full FSC Certification.

Figure 3.4 Douglas fir cladding on office building in Herefordshire.
Architects: Architype
Photo © Leigh Simpson

While home-grown softwoods are attractive in reducing the transport energy otherwise required for imported woods, they may not have the same qualities of strength or durability as the imported species because they will generally have been grown more quickly in the UK climate. For instance home-grown Douglas fir is not rated as durable as north American and home-grown European larch will not be as dense, strong, or knot free as Siberian-grown larch.

Figure 3.5 Home-grown larch cladding at Greenwich Millennium School
Edward Cullinen Architects
Photo © ECA

Other softwoods are coming onto the market, eg radiata pine, western hemlock, southern yellow pine, Californian redwood, that have suitable properties for cladding but are as yet rarely used in the UK. The majority however are only slightly durable (other than Californian redwood) and will therefore require treatment with preservative.

3.2.4 Temperate hardwoods

There is increasing use of durable temperate hardwoods such as European oak or sweet chestnut for cladding. European oak is readily available either home-grown or imported from other parts of Europe, particularly France, Germany or eastern Europe. Home-grown oak may not be generally obtainable in the lengths possible with imported wood, and this should be considered when designing the cladding layout. It is rated as a durable timber and can be used untreated for cladding providing sapwood is excluded. As a medium movement wood it will tend to develop small surface checks due to variation in moisture content but this will not affect its durability.

Although American white oak is technically suitable for use as external cladding, most of the supplies available in the UK are dried to levels suitable only for internal environments. If this timber is selected, care should be taken to ensure that it can be sourced at an appropriate moisture content. It may not be sufficient to recondition timber previously dried to low moisture content levels.

Figure 3.6 Green oak cladding on SAS office building, Buckinghamshire
Brocklehurst Architects
Photo © Brocklehurst Architects

While kiln dried temperate hardwoods can be used, there is a considerable economy if the wood is used 'green' as this saves the cost of kiln drying, although this saving may be offset by a possible increase in the cost of the

Figure 3.7 Oak cladding at Kings College hostel, Cambridge
Architects: Nicholas Ray Associates
Photo © Peter Cook

fixings. Because boards used for cladding are relatively thin they will air dry quite rapidly after installation but in the process the boards will shrink and tend to distort if not firmly restrained. It is important to make sufficient allowance for this movement by using narrow boards and keeping fixings relatively close together. The fixings must also be designed to absorb this shrinkage without the boards developing stresses that can lead to splitting. Since the boards will tend to distort as well as shrink, fixings should be close enough along the length of the board to restrain these natural tendencies as the wood dries.

The other characteristic of using European oak or sweet chestnut, particularly if used green is that both woods contain a great deal of tannin which will exude from the wood after installation. This will appear as a brown deposit on the face of the boards which will be gradually washed down by rainfall. This can be a particular problem if it is deposited on porous surfaces, such as brick or stone, below. Tannin may continue to be exuded for many months, and it is therefore advisable to protect surfaces below during this period. While it is possible to remove the staining from masonry or concrete, this can be a laborious and time-consuming process.

Tannin is also very corrosive to ferrous metals and corrosion can result in iron staining of the timber which is very difficult to remove. It is advisable to use corrosion resistant fixings, such as stainless steel for these timbers, whether used in dried or 'green' form.

Historically English elm was used for external cladding boards, but despite often lasting for many decades without any signs of decay it is classified as a non-durable timber and is therefore not currently deemed suitable for cladding, probably indicating that the British Standards overestimate the risk of decay in wood used for cladding. As the wood is now in relatively short supply in the British Isles due to Dutch elm disease, its use for cladding is now limited anyway.

Figure 3.8 Tannin exudation on European oak boards, River and Rowing Museum, Henley on Thames
David Chipperfield Architects

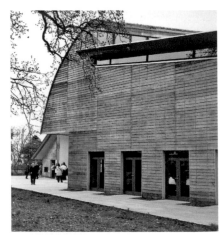

Figure 3.9 Tannin exudation during early weathering of building facade. Note use of planting areas below cladding to reduce splashing and to avoid staining of paving
Architects: Architype
Photo © Architype

3.2.5 Tropical hardwoods

In the past, there has been a wide range of tropical hardwoods used for timber cladding, although less frequently used than softwood and generally limited to more prestigious buildings. Concern about the sustainability of many of these has limited their use. However, there are now tropical timbers being imported with full certification of sustainable management whether plantation grown or 'secondary' species. These secondary species are less well known but have similar characteristics of durability, strength, and hardness as the better-known timbers. Some of the traditional tropical hardwoods may be grown in plantations that are not in their indigenous countries which may affect some of their basic properties of density, colour and durability. Confirmation may need to be sought that they are still suitable when used for cladding.

Figure 3.10 Angelim cladding, Lewis Glucksman gallery, University College, Cork
Architects: O'Donnell + Tuomey
Photo P Hislop

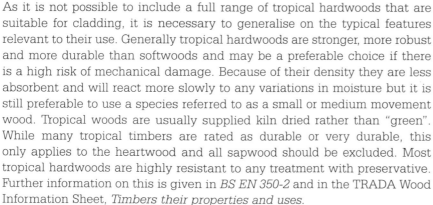

As it is not possible to include a full range of tropical hardwoods that are suitable for cladding, it is necessary to generalise on the typical features relevant to their use. Generally tropical hardwoods are stronger, more robust and more durable than softwoods and may be a preferable choice if there is a high risk of mechanical damage. Because of their density they are less absorbent and will react more slowly to any variations in moisture but it is still preferable to use a species referred to as a small or medium movement wood. Tropical woods are usually supplied kiln dried rather than "green". While many tropical timbers are rated as durable or very durable, this only applies to the heartwood and all sapwood should be excluded. Most tropical hardwoods are highly resistant to any treatment with preservative. Further information on this is given in *BS EN 350-2* and in the TRADA Wood Information Sheet, *Timbers their properties and uses*.

Figure 3.11 Iroko cladding, Royal Veterinary College LIVE Centre, Hatfield
Nicholas Hare Architects LLP
Photo © Lance McNulty

All the tropical hardwoods, whatever their original colour, will eventually weather to grey when exposed unfinished, although some will darken initially. While tropical hardwoods can be satisfactorily finished with coatings, care must be taken with the oilier woods, such as iroko and teak. It is likely that coatings on hardwoods may require more frequent maintenance than when used on softwoods as they do not absorb penetrating stains as readily. If the bleached colour is acceptable, they are better left unfinished and should not then require any maintenance for the lifetime of

Figure 3.12 Iroko cladding, Temple Bar, Dublin
Photo P Hislop

the building. Other than bleaching out the natural colour, exposure to ultra-violet light will not significantly affect the surface of these hardwoods but the increased uptake or loss of moisture in unfinished wood can lead to some surface checking.

Because these woods are denser and stronger than softwoods, thinner sections can be used and tongued or rebated profiles are less likely to be damaged during construction or in use.

3.3 Quality of timber

The appearance, strength and durability of timber cladding will depend on specifying a suitable quality of material as well as the choice of species. The visual quality of timber is largely related to the frequency and size of knots, the slope of grain, and the surface finish, ie whether planed, fine or rough sawn. If for instance a precise, smooth, flush face appearance is required it is preferable to use boards with straight grain and precise edges and limits on the size and frequency of knots. However if a more robust appearance is required, overlapping sawn boards, used vertically or horizontally, may be more appropriate and in this case larger and more frequent knots and the occasional rough arris may be acceptable. However loose or dead knots should always be excluded whatever visual quality is required.

It is important to decide on the visual effect at an early stage of the design because this will determine the quality of wood required and consequently the species that would be most suitable. It may not be possible, for instance, to tightly limit the size and frequency of knots in some woods. Over-specifying the quality of the wood can lead to high costs and cause conflict with suppliers. This is because merchants traditionally buy timber based on "shipping" grades which allow a much wider range of quality within each grade than prescribed under the British Standards for joinery. Timber cladding tends to be somewhere between "carpentry" and "joinery", and the timber industry is not used to supplying timber based on its appearance alone, although it may fully understand structural grading.

Currently *BS 1186-3 Timber for and workmanship in joinery. Specification for wood trim and its fixing* is the appropriate standard for defining the quality of timber cladding and trim. Under this standard wood is graded as CSH, Class 1, 2 or 3. These classes are largely defined by the acceptable size and frequency of knots although CSH virtually eliminates visual knots altogether by limiting them to a maximum of 6 mm diameter. Traditionally Class 3 has been considered adequate for cladding boards, but Class 2 is becoming more common where unfinished timber or transparent stains are to be used. On more prestigious buildings, Class 1 may be preferred for planed, and possibly unfinished boards but although this may be easily available in Douglas fir and western red cedar, it is more difficult to obtain this quality in European redwood, whitewood or European larch and could therefore prove expensive on what are otherwise low-cost species. Class CSH is largely intended for the manufacture of small profiled sections on which any knots could result in difficult machining or significant loss of strength and it is not appropriate for cladding boards. For temperate hardwoods such as European oak, it may be possible to achieve Class 1 by careful selection although Class 2 would be more typical. Tropical hardwoods are more generally available to Class 1 quality.

Revisions to this standard may eliminate these classes and cross refer to *BS EN 15146 Solid softwood panelling and cladding. Machined profiles without tongue and groove.* (Note it is not clear at this time whether there will be a separate standard for tongue and groove boards, for hardwoods or for western red cedar cladding). *BS 15146* differs from *BS 1186-3* in that, whilst still specifying the sizes and frequency of knots and other natural characteristics of wood, such as the acceptability of end splits, shakes and checks, and the presence of resin pockets, it relates these to each species and merely defines two grades, A and B. Although the standard also includes notional profiles they do not match many commercially available profiles or necessarily represent good practice in the design of purpose-made profiles.

The acceptability of such characteristics as the inclusion of sapwood will relate to whether the wood is to be treated with preservatives or not. The durability ratings of timber species refer to the heartwood only; generally sapwood should be excluded in the specification for timber which is to be used without treatment. However, it is not always possible to obtain timber totally devoid of sapwood and where the inclusion is very minor and does not represent a serious risk of decay, a slight relaxation may be acceptable. The following guidelines may be appropriate:

Figure 3.13 Pale coloured sapwood in hardwood cladding boards

- No sapwood should be visible on the exposed board face
- Sapwood which occupies less than 5 mm of the hidden board face or edge is unlimited
- Sapwood on hidden board surfaces which exceeds 5 mm should not be continuous for more than 500 mm
- It is always advisable to refer to the class required when specifying timber to be used for cladding; including, adding or redefining the clauses as necessary.

The European product standard, *BS EN 14915 Solid wood panelling and cladding – Characteristics, evaluation of conformity and marking* covers certification to particular performance requirements, such as reaction to fire, formaldehyde and pentachlorophenol content, water permeability and thermal conductivity. In the UK, the need for fire protection will depend on the context; a moderately durable or durable timber does not require preservative treatment; and the vapour permeability and thermal conductivity of the wood are largely irrelevant if there is a ventilated cavity behind the cladding. This standard may therefore have limited relevance to common practice in the UK, although the clauses covering preservative treatments, control of manufacture and good practice in construction are relevant.

It is recommended that, for any project, the contractor should be instructed to provide sufficient samples of the timber to be used for cladding prior to purchasing the material in order to agree on the acceptable visual quality typical of the material and profile to be supplied. It is particularly useful in determining the quality of wood to be supplied by timber merchants who are often unfamiliar with standards other than structural. Prior to installation on the building it is also advisable to require the contractor to provide a mock-up of the cladding large enough to illustrate typical conditions, such as butt joints and openings, as well as including reasonably long lengths of board. The provision of a sample panel is an effective way of proving that the desired appearance of the cladding can be achieved and ensuring that an acceptable quality is agreed between the designer and the contractor.

It may also be useful in that viewing the cladding in a simulated form may allow some compromise in the specification or design thereby improving the practicality of erection or manufacture, or reducing the cost of the cladding system.

Where wood is to be used undried, such as 'green' European oak, it may be advisable on large projects to build a substantial sample panel consisting of the type of boards to be used on the project. If these are acceptable in quality they can be left exposed to weather while the cladding is erected on the building. Some 'green' boards may distort or discolour unacceptably after fixing and boards can then be taken off the sample panel as replacements which will then reasonably match the weathered boards on the building.

4 Protection

4.1 Preservative pre-treatments

The key source of information is *BS 8417 Preservation of timber Recommendations*. It provides guidance on the treatment of timber for use in the UK, and refers to other vital parts of relevant BS and BS EN documents. Service factors based on safety and economic considerations have been developed in the standards framework and are set out in *BS 8417*. These allow a service life of up to 60 years to be specified. The specifier should use this guidance when assessing the level of durability required, regardless of whether this is achieved by treating the wood with preservative or selecting a naturally durable species of timber.

Although methods and types of preservative treatment are outlined in *BS 8417*, some of the preservatives, such as CCA, are no longer approved and others have been developed since the standard was published. The Wood Protection Association (WPA) Manual *Industrial wood preservation specification and practice includes* guidance on selection, specification and recommendations for treatment of timber commodities, including cladding, together with details of current preservative product names and suppliers.

The most effective methods of applying preservative to solid wood or suitable wood-based panels are either by immersion or pressure and vacuum methods, with pressure and double vacuum treatments being the more effective. If the wood is to be left unfinished, water-borne copper-organic treatments should always be used, but these will tend to leave a greenish tinge to the wood which will only fade with time. This preservative must be fully dried before the wood is handled.

If the cladding is to be finished with a protective surface coating system of paint or stain, traditionally light organic solvent preservatives have been used, also applied by either vacuum and pressure or immersion treatments. Because they are spirit based, organic solvent treatments do not increase the moisture content of the wood and therefore the risk of distortion of profiled sections is reduced. This treatment should also be fully dried before the wood is handled.

However, to reduce the use of organic solvents, waterborne micro-emulsion preservatives are now available. These have similar properties to the organic solvent formulations and are a suitable treatment, providing that they are protected with an applied coating system.

Another option is to use boron salts as a preservative, but this treatment is only rated as suitable for a 30 year life, even when protected with a surface coating system. Boron salts are soluble in water and are therefore somewhat susceptible to leaching. For this reason the timber should be protected by a surface coating system.

Low pressure spraying or brushing of a preservative pre-treatment is not acceptable, except on limited areas of freshly exposed pressure treated timber resulting from site cutting, planing or drilling. It should be noted here that surface coatings referred to as "preservative stains" and the like may not provide protection against fungal attack other than surface moulds and fungi which can disfigure the surface. It may be advisable to add an end grain sealer in addition to the coating system.

4.2 Modified timber

There are now several alternatives to using naturally durable or preservatively treated wood to achieve the necessary durability required for cladding. The advantage of these techniques is that cheap and plentiful, but not naturally durable species, can be used without the need to add traditional chemical preservatives.

Figure 4.1 Heat treated Thermowood® cladding at Villiers Hall, Nottingham
Photo © Vincent Timber Ltd

Other advantages are that the protection extends right through the wood, unlike preservative treatment which only penetrates to a limited depth. The wood also becomes more resistant to moisture absorption, resulting in less moisture movement than typical of untreated wood. In some species the modification process tends to darken the wood somewhat.

4.2.1 Heat treated timber

One method is to dry wood then heat to a very high temperature which reduces or denatures the natural nutritional content of the wood; the attraction for both fungi and insects. Timbers such as European redwood or European whitewood, both classified as slightly durable, after this form of drying acquire a resistance to attack which is superior to the natural durability of many other species. The treated material is suitable for use in Hazard Class 3 (above ground, not covered) with a service life of 30 years.

Currently two similar processes are carried out by companies in Finland and the Netherlands, and standard ranges of cladding board profiles are offered by the manufacturers.

Figure 4.2 Thermowood® cladding
Photo © Finnforest UK Ltd

The wood after treatment becomes slightly softer and more brittle, similar to western red cedar, but is quite strong enough for use as cladding. Swelling and shrinkage is only 50% that of the untreated species. The wood darkens initially due to the drying process, but will eventually bleach out to grey when exposed to ultraviolet light if left unfinished. The manufacturers also offer battens of the same material, but because of the relatively soft brittle nature of the material, better nail or screw retention can be achieved with conventional treated softwood battens.

4.2.2 Chemical modification

Another method of ensuring the durability of otherwise non-durable species is to impregnate the wood with chemicals which react with the wood substance and render it more durable, improving qualities such as moisture resistance and hence dimensional stability. The improved stability also improves coating performance, increasing maintenance intervals required between recoatings.

Figure 4.3 Chemically modified Accoya® samples
Photo © BSW Timber

One such process is acetylation which involves pressure impregnating pine with acetic anhydride which is derived from acetic acid (vinegar) to produce a product achieving a Class 1 durability rating to *BS EN 350-2*.

4.3 Surface protection

Surface coatings can simulate natural wood colours and in a transparent or translucent form will show the natural figure and texture of the wood. Opaque finishes are available in a wide range of colours and can provide a visual contrast to the more muted colour of materials such as brick, stone, slate or clay tiles.

Figure 4.4 Coloured stain finishes on horizontal boarding
Photo © Architype

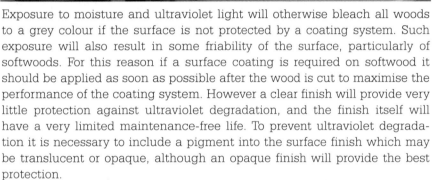

Figure 4.5 Coloured paints and stains on beach huts at Southwold

Exposure to moisture and ultraviolet light will otherwise bleach all woods to a grey colour if the surface is not protected by a coating system. Such exposure will also result in some friability of the surface, particularly of softwoods. For this reason if a surface coating is required on softwood it should be applied as soon as possible after the wood is cut to maximise the performance of the coating system. However a clear finish will provide very little protection against ultraviolet degradation, and the finish itself will have a very limited maintenance-free life. To prevent ultraviolet degradation it is necessary to include a pigment into the surface finish which may be translucent or opaque, although an opaque finish will provide the best protection.

Dark colours are effective in protecting against ultraviolet light but they will generate a higher temperature in the surface of wood exposed to the sun. This causes a reduction in the surface moisture content and can lead to cracking or "checking", and in some woods, resin exudation.

If a coating system is to be used it is advisable to apply at least one finish coat to all faces prior to fixing. This has the advantage that if shrinkage occurs, uncoated surfaces will not be exposed, (see *Figure 3.3*) but it also means that any moisture loss or pick-up is more likely to be more consistent on all faces.

It is important that any coating system is both extensible and permeable to moisture vapour. 'Traditional' general-purpose solvent-borne paints, stains or varnishes are too brittle (upon ageing) to follow moisture movement of the wood and will crack if this occurs. This can lead to moisture penetration and, because these coatings are less vapour permeable, moisture can become trapped behind the coating leading to possible degradation of the wood

Figure 4.6 Proprietary pre-finished
cladding panels
Photos © Vincent Timber Ltd

and blistering, flaking or peeling of the finish. Modern microporous finishes are flexible enough to follow any moisture movement of the wood, and sufficiently permeable to prevent build-up of moisture in the wood. If these stains are applied to fine sawn surfaces they will generally last longer than if applied to planed surfaces, although this may require more stain initially.

Modern coating systems, ie basecoats or primers and their respective finishes, applied under controlled conditions in the factory, can extend the maintenance period significantly. Coating systems applied on-site are more subject to deterioration because the surface of the wood may have been exposed to ultraviolet light and weather, plus a possible accumulation of dirt or construction dust. On-site there is no way that the moisture content can be controlled within a range suitable for the application of the coating system and quality of workmanship is not always predictable. Basecoats, even when factory-applied, provide limited protection against moisture and ultraviolet light.

Once any coating system begins to deteriorate it is important to re-coat before the bare surface of the wood becomes exposed. If left to this stage, any subsequent coating system will not achieve the same adhesion and will therefore require earlier maintenance. This is more obvious on softwoods where ultraviolet light can affect the surface of the wood more severely than with hardwoods. However, generally low-build basecoats or finishes will not last as long on hardwoods because it is not possible to achieve the same penetration into the denser woods.

For more information on suitable finishes for external timber cladding, see TRADA Wood Information Sheet, *Finishes for external timber*.

4.4 Unfinished timber

As an alternative to coating the timber it can be left unfinished to weather and bleach naturally. Most hardwoods and many softwoods can be left unfinished and if the appearance of the bleached timber is acceptable, no further maintenance will be required. There may be more movement in the timber, due to increased moisture pick-up, which can lead to some surface checking (small cracks in the surface which will open and close depending on the moisture content). In polluted environments, dirt can also be more readily picked up by unfinished wood eventually resulting in blackening of the surface. The rate of surface bleaching can also be uneven due to shading from projections such as eaves, balconies and sills or even surface mounted objects such as lights, rainwater heads etc. 'Green' timber is generally left unfinished, but in timbers with a high tannin content, such as European oak, the considerable run-off of tannin during the bleaching process should be considered (see Section 3.2.4). It is important to avoid this tannin run-off staining porous surfaces below by design or temporary protection during the weathering process.

The rate that timber bleaches will also depend to some extent on orientation and on north, north east, or north west elevations, the process can take much longer than on south, south east, or south west elevations. Sometimes the proximity of other buildings leading to shading can affect the rate of surface bleaching.

In close proximity to trees or heavy vegetation, or where there is an unusually high run-off of moisture, unfinished timber, particularly of the more permeable species, can blacken and it may be necessary to apply a moisture-resistant coating and possibly an anti-fungal wash to limit this effect. Either of these finishes may require re-application at intervals to remain effective.

Air pollution from exhausts can also cause blackening, and it is not advisable to use unfinished timber where there is a high level of pollution expected. Other pollutants such as brake dust from cars or trains which contains metals, can react with the tannins in some timbers, resulting in iron staining. Some cases of the surfaces of unfinished timber blackening have been found to be due to cement dust from nearby construction work. There are cleaning fluids available which will remove staining, and to some extent the bleaching of timber surfaces, but will not prevent further discolouration in the future, unless the source is eliminated or the environment is changed in some way.

The durability of the timber is not affected by the bleaching process. There are many historical examples of unfinished softwood or hardwood cladding that have lasted many centuries without deterioration, often in areas exposed to a high level of ultraviolet attack such as timber clad Alpine buildings.

4.5 Fire protection

The use of external timber cladding is governed by Building Regulations and Standards. All UK Regulations have rules limiting the area of "unprotected cladding" ie combustible materials such as wood, permitted in proximity to boundaries. Timber cladding closer than 1 m to a boundary should meet Class 0 (National Standard) or Class B (European Class) or better. Buildings above a certain height may have additional requirements. The regulations for each area should be checked for details.

A number of products are available to control the surface spread of flame resistance to Class 0 or Euroclass B; the most suitable for cladding being vacuum/pressure impregnation treatments. A leach-resistant treatment is recommended. Humidity-resistant types may be suitable but for external use these require a surface coating that is maintained in service.

The penetration and therefore the effectiveness of these treatments depend to some extent on the natural permeability of the wood. Sapwood is generally more easily treated than heartwood and the heartwood of some dense softwoods, such as European larch are quite resistant to treatment. Hardwoods used for cladding are generally too dense to accept treatment. Manufacturers will advise which timber species and thicknesses are certified for Class 0 or Euroclass B.

Further information is given in the *WPA manual Industrial flame retardant treatment of solid timber and panel products*.

Cavity barriers may be required in certain locations behind timber cladding, such as at compartment floors or around window openings to restrict the movement and penetration of smoke and flame. The requirements may differ between England and Wales, Scotland and Northern Ireland and the appropriate regulations should therefore be consulted.

It may be necessary to provide cavity barriers across ventilated cavities at upper floor levels, but this should not restrict ventilation and drainage to the cavity above. It may be necessary to close off the cavity at floor level but provide gaps for ventilating the cavity below, and another gap above the barrier to ventilate and drain the cavity above. It may be possible largely to conceal these gaps in the design of the cladding profiles eg open jointed horizontal boards or vertical board-on-board. With a board-on-board arrangement this can be done by incorporating a horizontal batten of a combined thickness of the inner board and the cavity behind at the base of the cladding. There will still be sufficient ventilation and drainage of the cavity above this batten. Similarly with horizontal open jointed boards a batten can be used to close the cavity at the bottom as sufficient ventilation and drainage can take place through the "open" joint above. In both cases the top of the extra batten should be chamfered to direct any water in the cavity to the outside.

There are a number of cavity barriers that are based on intumescent tapes or paints which normally will provide a sufficient clear path for ventilation and drainage behind the cladding. In fire conditions the intumescent material will expand and block the gaps. This solution is acceptable to many building control authorities but it is always advisable to discuss what is acceptable locally at an early design stage.

Where timber cladding passes the end of a party or separating wall, the cavity between the cladding and the wall should be closed by a vertical timber batten or mineral wool.

5 Detail design

Probably the primary concern of anyone designing a timber-clad building is to ensure that the material will be sufficiently durable to provide the desired service life without an excessive level of maintenance.

UK Building Regulations and Standards recommend that materials likely to be adversely affected by moisture, eg non durable species or the sapwood of any species, should be protected by preservative treatment. However, the primary means of ensuring durability should always be by correct design. Reliance on natural durability or the addition of a preservative should be regarded as a second line of defence.

5.1 Control of moisture

All timber cladding should be designed as a rainscreen in principle. This assumes that the cladding will always be subject to some penetration of moisture, and therefore a separate weatherproof membrane will be necessary behind, although largely protected from wind, rain and daylight by the cladding. If there is a masonry wall behind the cladding, a separate membrane is not usually necessary. The amount of moisture that penetrates will depend on the design of the cladding, an open-jointed system obviously allowing more moisture penetration than, for instance, an overlapping design. Whatever system is used an open cavity should always be provided behind the cladding to allow for the drainage of any moisture that penetrates the cladding and to provide sufficient ventilation to dissipate any internally generated vapour. Ventilating the cavity will mean that both external and internal faces of the cladding are exposed to the same ambient humidity and consequently will have a similar moisture content. This will reduce any natural tendency of the wood to distort due to a variation of the moisture content on opposite faces.

If the moisture content of wood is held below 22% there is no risk in the UK of fungal attack, and little risk of attack by insects, although it may be subject to termite attack in other parts of the world. Limited exposure to wetting resulting in moisture contents higher than 22% will not instigate decay but sustained exposure above this level increases the risk of attack.

In the UK the typical ambient humidity and even direct exposure to rain, will not raise the average moisture content of timber above about 20% (*BS 1186-3* quotes a maximum level of 19% mc for wood unprotected externally).

Avoiding direct contact with porous surfaces or wetted non-porous surfaces will prevent wood absorbing moisture from these surfaces. This is particularly important if the end grain of wood is exposed because it is very absorbent. Either a damp proof membrane or a sufficient gap will provide this protection by preventing contact with wetted surfaces. Vertical boards should always be kept clear of any flashings below by at least 15 mm and also have the top edges well protected. Cutting the bottom of vertical boards at an angle will prevent water hanging on the underside where it could be absorbed by the end grain. Horizontal boards should also stop short of any vertical members by 8–10 mm to allow ventilation to the end grain of the boards.

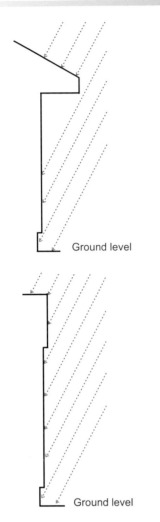

Figure 5.1 Protection from projecting roofs

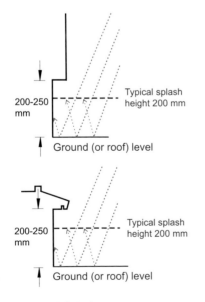

Figure 5.2 Splash zones

Projecting roofs may largely protect wall surfaces from direct wetting, but even with large projections wind is likely to drive water against lower surfaces. The overhang is more likely to extend the life of surface finishes rather than affect the overall durability of the wood. If the cladding is to be left unfinished, overhangs can prove to be a disadvantage as shading from the projection will slow, or even prevent, the natural weathering and bleaching of the wood compared to the unprotected areas of the wall and result in uneven colouring.

Indirect wetting, as a result of splashing off the ground or other horizontal surfaces, such as roofs, below the cladding, may result in regular wetting of the lower boards which can lead to deterioration of surface finishes and possible algal growth. It is advisable to stop any wood cladding 200–250 mm above ground level, or abutting roofs, to prevent this form of wetting. More detailed information on these design principles is available in TRADA Wood Information Sheet, *Durability by design*.

5.2 Allowing for moisture movement

As an organic material, the moisture content of wood will always vary with changes in environmental conditions. External cladding may vary between a maximum of 22% on northern faces in winter and a minimum 10% on southern faces exposed to summer sun (although higher or lower percentages than these are occasionally recorded). The seasonal variation on any one face of the building does not normally vary by more than 6–8%. However, this change in moisture content is sufficient to cause swelling or shrinkage of the wood. This will not in itself affect the strength or durability of wood, unless the movement is restrained by fixings or tight jointing, in which case there is a risk of the wood splitting, cupping or bowing. Excessive moisture movement can reduce the overlap between boards or result in tongues becoming disengaged from grooves, reducing the weather resistance. If the tongue is the sole means of positioning the bottom of the board above, disengagement will compromise the fixing of the boards to the building. Sufficient allowance for moisture movement must be therefore provided in the detail design of any timber cladding.

The best way to reduce any problems of movement is to ensure that the moisture content of the boards when erected is as close as possible to the likely "in use" moisture content. As in the UK the normal range of moisture content of timber cladding in use is likely to be between 12% and 20% (*BS 1186-3* suggests 13–19%) a mean of about 16% should be the aim. As this can still represent a significant variation in size, the scale of the expected movement can be reduced by limiting the width of the boards to about 150 mm, particularly if the wood is to be used green. The joints between boards should be designed to accommodate the likely shrinkage and swelling of the boards whilst also ensuring that they remain weatherproof. An overlap or open-jointed cladding design is more tolerant of movement than rebated or tongued and grooved profiles. Any distortion of tongued and grooved boards may make it difficult to engage the tongues in the grooves during installation and any subsequent movement can result in the tongues splitting off. If tongued and grooved boards are to be used, the width of board should be further restricted, preferably to 100 mm, but certainly to a maximum of 125 mm. Only kiln dried wood at the recommended moisture content should be used for tongued and grooved profiles.

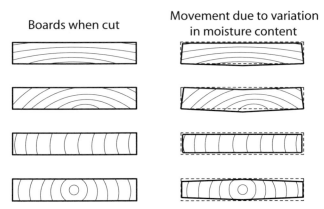

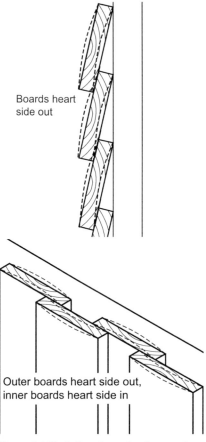

Boards heart
side out

Figure 5.3 Changes in shape of boards cut from different parts of a log with changes in moisture content

The design of fixings must also take into account the possible moisture movement of the board. Boards up to 100 mm wide can be single fixed whether they are overlapped or tongued and grooved because the board can swell or shrink either side of the single fixing without stresses developing. Wider boards will require double fixing to assist in keeping them flat. However, the wood between the fixings will be subject to stresses as a result of moisture movement. This natural tendency of boards to change shape due to moisture variation can be used to advantage if care is taken during installation. For most types of cladding, boards in which the growth rings run tangentially to the section should be used heart side out. The natural tendency is then for the centre of the boards to cup out from the plane of the cladding, rather than in, ensuring that the joints between the boards tighten rather than open up. However, with board-on-board cladding there is some advantage in using the inner boards with the heart side in as this will give better contact between the inner and outer boards if the boards shrink. Quarter sawn boards have the least risk of changing shape as a result of moisture movement, but it is generally uneconomic to use quarter sawn boards throughout.

Outer boards heart side out,
inner boards heart side in

Figure 5.4 Exploiting the natural properties of timber
top Horizontal boarding
bottom Vertical board-on-board cladding

5.3 Cladding support

The cavity behind any timber cladding should not be less than 19 mm wide but the width is usually determined by the size of battens necessary to accommodate the fixings for the boards. For standard nails the battens should be at least 2.5 times the thickness of the boards to be fixed, but with improved nails (eg annular ring-shank) or screws, a batten twice the thickness of the board is adequate. Generally battens to which the boards are fixed should be not less than 38 x 38 mm.

Support battens should not exceed 600 mm spacing, whether vertical or horizontal, to limit the span of the cladding board and therefore its thickness. For diagonal boards it is preferable if the batten centres do not exceed 400 mm, unless the battens are also fixed diagonally. Limiting the spacing of the support battens with the relatively close spacing of fixings will tend to restrain any natural tendency for the boards to twist, bow or cup. Also if boards are to be used green, batten centres should preferably be reduced to 400 mm or maximum 500 mm centres. Although single fixings are adequate for boards less than 100 mm wide, sections narrower than this may rotate around the single fixing and in this case it is advisable to reduce batten centres to 400 mm maximum spacing to resist this movement.

Figure 5.5 Horizontal boarding; office building, Herefordshire
Architects: Architype
Photo © Leigh Simpson

Figure 5.7 Cedar boarding, Greenwich Millennium Village
Ralph Erskine/EPR Architects
Photo P Hislop

Horizontal boards are fixed to vertical battens and these will not restrict either drainage or the vertical circulation of air in the cavity, providing that horizontal battens are omitted at the top and bottom of the cladding. If these are necessary to provide support for fixings for other components, they should be smaller than the vertical battens so as not to block the ventilation path (*Figures 5.5–5.7*).

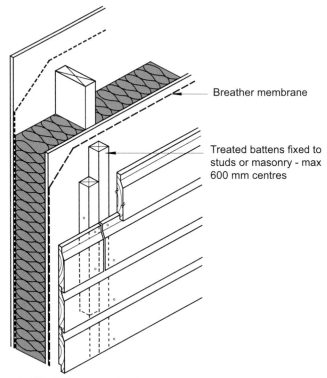

Breather membrane

Treated battens fixed to studs or masonry - max 600 mm centres

Figure 5.6 Typical construction: horizontal weatherboarding on vertical timber battens
Note: The drawing shows cladding details on conventional timber frame construction. For other forms of construction, the details outside the breather membrane are the same

Vertical boards will be fixed to horizontal battens and if the boards are tight-jointed, these would prevent drainage and vertical circulation of air and it is necessary to introduce vertical counter battens behind the horizontal battens (*Figures 5.8, 5.9*). Although a 12 mm minimum gap would theoretically be adequate between the horizontal battens and the inner wall, counter battens of solid wood should be increased in thickness to reduce the risk of the wood splitting when the battens are nailed through to studwork or masonry behind. If the horizontal battens are only to be fixed to the counter battens, rather than nailed through to timber studs behind, the counter battens must be of sufficient thickness to take the fixing nails. As the horizontal battens are unsupported other than by studs or counter battens, they should also be stiff enough not to flex unduly when the boards are nailed to them.

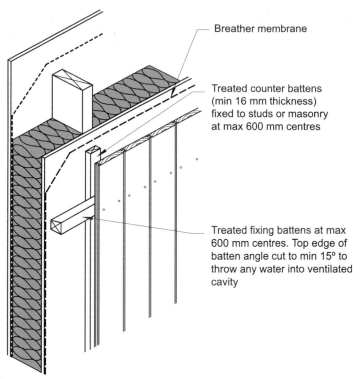

Breather membrane

Treated counter battens (min 16 mm thickness) fixed to studs or masonry at max 600 mm centres

Treated fixing battens at max 600 mm centres. Top edge of batten angle cut to min 15° to throw any water into ventilated cavity

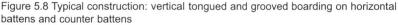

Figure 5.9 Vertical boarding, Formby Pool
Feilden Clegg Bradley Architects LLP
Photo © Feilden Clegg Bradley

Figure 5.8 Typical construction: vertical tongued and grooved boarding on horizontal battens and counter battens
Note: The drawing shows cladding details on conventional timber frame construction. For other forms of construction, the details outside the breather membrane are the same

If a board-on-board or an open-jointed type of vertical cladding is used it is not necessary to provide counter battens as there will be sufficient ventilation and drainage behind the outer boards, through the open joints (*Figures 5.10, 5.11*). In this case it is preferable if the horizontal battens are chamfered on the top edge to shed any water outwards. When counter battens are used, the horizontal battens should be chamfered to slope inwards and drain any water into the cavity behind the horizontal battens.

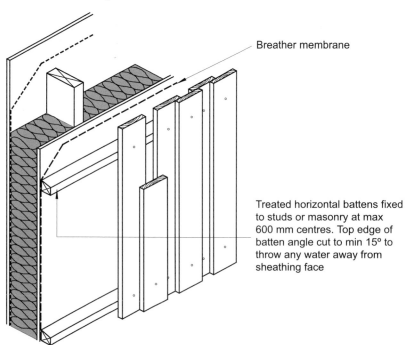

Breather membrane

Treated horizontal battens fixed to studs or masonry at max 600 mm centres. Top edge of batten angle cut to min 15° to throw any water away from sheathing face

Figure 5.10 Vertical board on board cladding, Seton Mains House
Paterson Architects
Photo © Keith Hunter Photography

Figure 5.11 Typical construction: board-on-board cladding on horizontal timber battens
Note: The drawing shows cladding details on conventional timber frame construction. For other forms of construction, the details outside the breather membrane are the same

Figure 5.12 Lapped boarding, Genesis building
Architects: Architype
Photo © Architype

Figure 5.13 Horizontal boarding provides surface modelling, Longwell Green Leisure Centre, Bristol
Architects: Feilden Clegg Bradley
Photo © Feilden Clegg Bradley

5.4 Board profiles

Although the strength of the species chosen has some bearing on the thickness of board, this thickness is more likely to be determined by the profile chosen. While square cut boards might be reduced to 16 mm thickness, rebated boards should never be less than 19 mm thick and standard tongued and grooved boards not less than 22 mm thick when used externally. However, tongued and grooved boards are now available with rebated shoulders below the tongue. This means that fixings can be made through this part of the profile, rather than through the tongue and the overall thickness can be reduced to 19 mm. The thin edge of feather-edged boards should never be less than 8 mm.

5.4.1 Horizontal boards

For horizontal boards not exceeding 150 mm width, the vertical overlaps on square or feather-edge boards should be a minimum of 25 mm. This is relevant to dried wood. If the wood is to be used green, with consequent shrinkage after installation, board width and overlap may need consideration. Single nailing may also be advisable despite the risk of cupping.

For shiplap or rebated feather edge boards, the overlap can be reduced to a minimum 15 mm but a 2 mm gap should be provided between the upstand or rebate to allow for possible expansion of the boards. The curved or chamfered shoulder to shiplap boards drains water away effectively and produces a strong shadowline.

Horizontal tongued and grooved boards should preferably be limited to 125 mm face width, with a minimum 10 mm deep tongue, and 2 mm clearance above the tongue and shoulder when installed to allow for possible expansion. Horizontal tongued and grooved boards should always be installed tongue uppermost with the shoulder of the board at the base of the tongue chamfered to shed water away from the tongue. The underside of the board should be square cut or slightly chamfered away from the tongue. The v-joint typical of internal tongued and grooved cladding is not suitable for horizontal use externally.

Horizontal open-jointed boards should have an 8–15 mm gap at the outer face. The top and bottom edges should preferably be chamfered to about 30° to ensure rapid run-off from the top edge and to prevent water running back on the underside. Chamfered edges also allow the boards to be slightly overlapped, reducing the view into the cavity and ensuring that a breather membrane behind is not exposed to direct sunlight. Some manufacturers of breather membranes require the gaps between horizontal boards to be limited to 10 mm maximum and will not offer their product for open-jointed vertical boards because of concern that long-term exposure to ultraviolet light will reduce the service life of the material.

Figure 5.14 Lapped boarding, The Old Woodyard, Norfolk
Architects: Studio MGM
Photo © Neil Winder

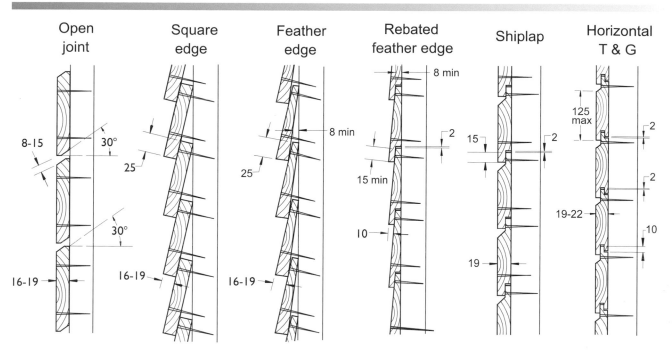

Figure 5.15 Horizontal boarding profiles

5.4.2 Diagonal boards

A shiplap profile is most appropriate for this application as the curved shoulder will effectively channel water away from the upstand, providing that it is sufficiently large. Simple overlapping boards are not suitable as they will let water through by capillary action or wind pressure. Tongued and grooved boards should be installed tongue up, but even so, water will tend to be drawn up the face of the tongues by capillary action which can result in sustained wetting of the joint.

For diagonal boards, the battens are sometimes fixed perpendicular to the boards to reduce the span of the board between fixings. This may improve drainage off the battens but does not eliminate the need for counter battens behind to provide ventilation.

Figure 5.16 Diagonal boarding, Chapel Idne Surf Shop, Cornwall
Wynter Cole Architects
Photo © P Dowling

5.4.3 Vertical boards

Although tongued and grooved boards work more effectively vertically they should also preferably not exceed 125 mm face width so that any moisture movement across the board width does not result in the tongues becoming disengaged. The tongues should be of the same size as those recommended for tongued and grooved boards used horizontally but the traditional v-joint can be used in this case. A rebated overlapping board similar to the horizontal shiplap board is frequently used for vertical boards in North Europe but rarely in the UK. Providing that there is a minimum 20 mm overlap this profile works well vertically, and gives a strong shadow line.

The most versatile arrangement for vertical cladding is board-on-board. Simple rectangular boards can be used but the width of top or bottom boards can be varied to give different visual effects. The outer board can also be shaped in different ways to allow more modelling of the surface.

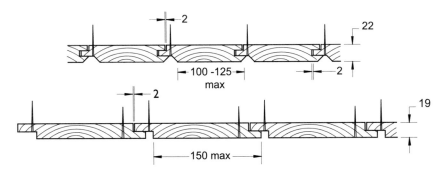

Figure 5.17 Profiles suitable for diagonal and vertical boarding

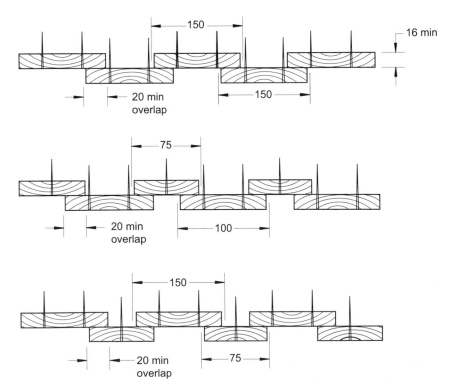

Figure 5.18 Profiles suitable for vertical boarding

The preferred overlap between outer and inner board should be 20–25 mm. An additional refinement is to run drainage grooves near the edges of both the inner and outer boards. When installed these grooves oppose each other and provide an effective pressure relief and drainage channel. With this additional grooving the board-on-board arrangement can work effectively as a roof finish.

Open jointed boards can be used vertically but increased rain penetration and ultraviolet exposure on breather membranes must be considered (see Section 5.4.1) as well as increased visibility into the cavity. The addition of an insect mesh directly behind the boards across the whole face of the wall can be an advantage.

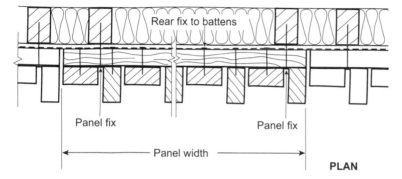

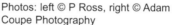

PLAN

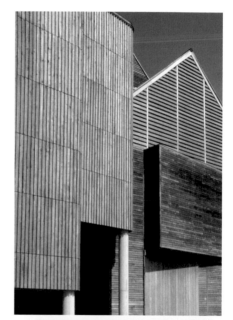

Figure 5.19 above, left and right
Vertical open jointed board on board green oak at National Maritime Museum, Falmouth
Photos: left © P Ross, right © Adam Coupe Photography

Figure 5.20 Vertical board on board cladding, Greenwich Millennium School. Edward Cullinan Architects
Photo © ECA

Figure 5.21 Vertical boarding on 'The Core' building, Eden project, Cornwall. Grimshaw Architects.
Photo © Adam Coupe Photography

5.5 Fixings

5.5.1 Softwood

Softwood boards are normally nailed to treated softwood battens. Standard wire nails can be used but annular ring-shank nails are preferred for their improved holding power. Small head, or siding nails are suitable for most softwoods, but larger heads are recommended for western red cedar because small heads can tend to pull through this soft wood. Some pneumatically-driven nails have D-shaped heads rather than round heads which affects the appearance of the fixing and may not be acceptable visually. Pneumatically-driven virtually headless pins are not recommended for fixing cladding boards.

Nail penetration into the batten should normally be 2 times the thickness of the board being fixed with annular rink-shank nails (2.5 times when round wire nails are used). Nails should be driven marginally below the surface to compensate for possible shrinkage of the wood which may otherwise cause the nail heads to stand proud of the surface. Nail fixings should be at least 20 mm from the end of the boards and 15 mm from the edges.

Secret nailing with single nails is not recommended for conventional tongued and grooved boards because of the risk of the tongue splitting. If a rebated tongue and groove board is used, nails can be driven through the shoulder and will be concealed by the overlap of the board above.

Overlapping boards above 100 mm width should be double nailed. Nails should preferably be located at the quarter points in the board width, but it is important that where boards are overlapped, or in a board-on-board pattern, that the nails fixing the outer boards do not penetrate the inner boards, as moisture movement will be in opposing directions and can lead to splitting of these boards.

For all boards to be left unfinished austenitic stainless steel nails should be used in order to avoid long term rust stains on the wood. This is especially important on woods with a high tannin content, where the reaction between the tannin and any ferrous metal will produce purple-black staining which cannot be removed. Stainless steel will weather to a matt grey colour similar to that of bleached wood, reducing the visibility of the nails in the long term.

Even if the cladding is to have a surface coating, stainless steel nails are preferred, rather than plated steel, because galvanising or other plating can be damaged when the nails are driven home manually or pneumatically, leading to possible corrosion. The typical low-build stain coatings applied to cladding also may not provide much long term protection to fixings.

5.5.2 Hardwood

Hardwood boards are normally fixed by screwing to treated softwood fixing battens. Even for boards installed at a moisture content close to their in-use range, it is advisable to pre-drill holes in the boards to provide a clearance around the shank of the screw to allow for seasonal variations in moisture content. The head of a countersunk screw will normally provide sufficient retention but using larger diameter screws with bigger heads is preferred for this reason. Restricting the board width to a maximum 150 mm, and locating the screws at the quarter points of the board width, will limit the width of wood that will swell or shrink between the screws. A 2 mm clearance between the shank of the screw and the hole in the board should be adequate for woods rated as small or medium movement if the boards are installed at about the recommended 16% moisture content.

However if the wood is to be used green, considerable shrinkage may take place between the fixings during the initial drying stage. It is advisable in this case to pre-drill the boards to provide at least 4 mm clearance between the shank of the screw and the hole. As the head of a screw will not then be large enough to hold the board it will be necessary to fit washers under the screw heads in order to provide sufficient purchase. The washers can be slotted to allow them to move with the wood, although care must be taken in aligning the slots and ensuring that the screws are in the outer ends of the slots initially. Alternatively drilled washers can be set into recessed holes in the wood which are sufficiently oversized to allow movement between the washers and the wood. Roundhead or panhead screws are normally used with washers, but there are also various sheeting screws available with built in washers and these have been successfully used for fixing green wood. Some have the additional advantage of including a compressible rubber seal under the metal washer which will keep pressure on the boards even if they shrink in thickness. The use of large screws, particularly in conjunction with metal washers, will have a strong impact on the appearance of the cladding. While this might often be desirable, sometimes concealing the fixings is preferred. One way of achieving this is to assemble the boards into panels by screwing through the battens into the back of the boards. It is possible to get sufficient screw retention in the thickness of a hardwood board but this is not feasible with a softwood board. In this case adequate clearance holes must be provided in the battens rather than the boards. The completed panels can then be fitted to the face of the building, either by screwing back the battens through open joints between the boards or screwing right through both the boards and battens and pelleting these holes after the panels are in place.

An alternative method of concealing the fixings of horizontal boards is to mount the board on U-shaped stainless steel clips fixed to the vertical battens, which engage in a slot in the underside of the board. The top of the board is then held by screwing through the rebated upstand. This is a similar principle to tongued and grooved boarding, but the upstand of the clip can be long enough to allow for considerable shrinkage in the board width and is both easier to engage and less liable to damage than an extended tongue. An additional advantage is that the bottom edge of abutting boards fixed to the vertical batten can be held and aligned with a single wide clip. This system is suited to a shiplap or open joint type of boarding. The clip system however requires careful design for each application, taking into account the species, likely shrinkage, thickness of board and other characteristics.

All unfinished hardwood boards should be fixed with austenitic stainless steel screws and any washers or clips should be of the same material. Even if the boards are to be stained or painted, stainless steel screws are preferable to plated screws which can be damaged during installation, resulting in corrosion and consequent staining. If the boards are to be directly fixed to mild steel or galvanised members, electrolytic action may occur between the metals if stainless steel fixings are used. For this reason it is always preferable to introduce wood battens between the boards and any metal

Figure 5.22 Use of washers to allow movement in green oak
Photo: left T Hyland right © P Ross

Figure 5.23 Secret fixing of oak boarding University College of Mary Immaculate, Cork. Murray O'Laoire Architects
Bottom: Clip (superimposed) with position shown dotted
Photos © Murray O'Laoire Architects

framing. The boards can then still be fixed to the battens with stainless steel screws but plated screws or bolts can be used to fix the battens to the steelwork. Fixing directly to steel is particularly a problem with self drilling fixings which will result in unprotected mild steel swarf, which can corrode and cause iron staining, as well as electrolytic action between the different metals.

5.6 Insect mesh

The cavity behind timber cladding can provide a warm dry home for various types of insects such as wasps, woodlice and flies. The risk is dependent on factors such as the rural or urban location of the building, the proximity of trees, the height above the ground etc. For this reason TRADA does not advise on where protection may be required, but, if it is necessary, there are a number of ways of providing some protection against infestation.

At the openings at the top and bottom of any wall of close jointed horizontal boards a mesh can be fixed vertically at the back of the cavity and folded up and attached to the underside of the vertical battens. Similarly, with close jointed vertical boards, the mesh can be attached vertically to the wall behind the counter battens, and folded out and fixed to the horizontal battens.

With board-on-board vertical cladding, the mesh can be attached to horizontal bottom battens, and extended out to run continuously across the inner boards, sealing the gaps behind the outer boards.

With horizontal overlapping boards (square or feather-edge), there will always be a triangular gap at the ends of the boards through which insects can enter. One solution is to use a compressible foam tape between the ends of the boards and the last vertical batten, or alternatively to use a fabric mesh stapled to the battens over the whole façade before fixing the boards.

This last method is the only practical method of preventing insect access through any open-jointed boarding system. In this case it has the additional advantages of reducing rain penetration, shading the cavity from ultraviolet light, and restricting visibility into the cavity.

5.7 Relating timber cladding to building configuration

The overall visual quality of timber cladding will be very dependent on the associated details relating to building configuration such as corners, changes of level, parapets, openings, soffits, junctions with other materials etc. These conditions need careful consideration, particularly in relating the natural dimensions of the cladding system to other elements of the building.

5.7.1 Board layout

Non-orthogonal shapes, ie curved surfaces in plan, section or elevation, or angled facades require careful choice of cladding and may determine whether vertical, horizontal or even diagonal board layouts are the most practical.

Figure 5.24 Western red cedar boarding on the curved facade of the Weald and Downland gridshell
Edward Cullinan Architects
Photo © ECA

Vertical boards are more suited to curved plans and for tight radii, board on board is more suitable than tongued and grooved because of the difficulty in engaging tongues on a curve. For very tight radii, the width of the boards should also be reduced. The simplest way of accommodating these curves in the horizontal battens is to build these up in two or more layers which can be bent around the curved plan. The successive layers can be nailed together, but it is important that joints in each layers do not coincide. If a building is curved in section, horizontal boards are more appropriate but overlap boards or shiplap profiles are preferable to tongued and grooved as these may not engage properly on a curved surface. If horizontal boards are used at too shallow an angle on a building curved in section, water may be driven up the overlap and drain into the cavity. Capillary action can also draw moisture up into any joints at a shallow angle resulting in sustained high moisture content in the joint.

A shallow angle pitched façade or gable can be more easily accommodated by cutting the ends of vertical boards, than tapering horizontal boards, but for steeper angles either method is suitable. With horizontal boards an additional batten must follow the pitch of the slope to support the tapered ends of boards. The use of diagonal boards can sometimes simplify the junction with sloping planes.

Figure 5.25 Curved facades of vertical board on board green oak. Falmouth Maritime Museum
Architects: Long and Kentish
Photo: © Long and Kentish

5.7.2 Board lengths

The availability of boarding in long lengths will depend largely on the species chosen. Softwoods such as European redwood or whitewood, European larch or Douglas fir are normally available in up to 4.8 m lengths. Temperate hardwoods such as European oak or sweet chestnut, are generally limited to 2.0 – 4.0 m but with a maximum of 5 m. Tropical hardwoods are generally available from 2.1 – 4.2 m lengths, depending on species (although longer lengths can sometimes be obtained; maximum 4.8 m).

Horizontal boards, of whatever species, will probably need to be end-jointed on most projects. Although joints will have to be coincident with the supporting battens, the width of a standard batten will not provide sufficient space for the fixing of abutting boards, within acceptable limits of end distance for fixings on the board, or on the edge distance for the battens.

There are various ways of resolving this. All boards can be cut to consistent lengths so that butt joints all occur on a single line. In this case two vertical battens can be used alongside each other, but gapped equivalent to the gap between the ends of boards. (With timber frame construction, where the joint line lies on the centre of a stud, it may be necessary to use a single wide batten that can be fixed through the sheathing to the stud behind.) 'Panellising' the cladding in this way requires the vertical end joints to be carefully determined, because these will have a noticeable visual impact, and will need to be related to openings etc. This will make prefabrication of the wall easier if this is an advantage, but it is likely to be more expensive due to the waste involved in cutting all the boards to the same length.

If the intention is to play down butt joints, and make the wall finish appear more monolithic, the board lengths should coincide with batten spacing, but where a butt joint occurs, a short length of the standard batten section can be nailed to the side of the full height batten (*Figure 5.6*). The length

Figure 5.26 Panellised cladding, Princes Royal sports arena, Boston
Photo © Finnforest UK Ltd

should be at least three times the board width. The end of one board can then be fixed to the full height batten and the end of the other to the additional section of batten. For visual reasons, the butt joint positions should be staggered, so they do not occur directly one above the other. Whichever method is chosen, a minimum gap of 5 mm should be left between ends of boards for ventilation and drainage of the end grain.

Butt joints at the ends of vertical boards tend to become increasingly visible in the long term because water run-off from the upper board tends to wet and swell the end grain of the board below. This effect can be reduced by chamfering the ends of boards to discharge water to the outside face, possibly sealing the top of the lower board and leaving a wider gap between, eg 5–8 mm. Board lengths need to coincide with the position of horizontal battens, and the addition of a short length of batten to the top of the standard batten, will provide space for the additional fixings for the bottom of the upper board.

Alternatively, board lengths could be arranged to coincide with storey heights. This usually means that it is not necessary to have butt joints within typical floor to ceiling height for most species. Offcuts of boards can usually be used economically under window panels etc, and this may therefore prove less expensive than standardising horizontal board lengths. Another advantage is that as all buildings tend to suffer some shrinkage, deflection or creep, the break at floor level can be used to take up any vertical movement of the structure. It may also simplify the introduction of cavity barriers separating the upper and lower storey height cladding.

With hardwood in particular, it is probable that techniques such as finger jointing or end dowelling will become more common and economic, allowing boards to be made up into much longer lengths, overcoming the need to butt joint as frequently, or cut lengths of board to waste.

5.7.3 Junctions with other materials

Where timber cladding with a cavity behind abuts walls of other materials, either at re-entrants or in line, it is not usually necessary to introduce an additional dpc if there is already a breather membrane which can be extended around to the edge of the wall and held tight against it by a vertical batten. This applies if the connection is to the outer leaf of a cavity wall, but if the cavity is in line, or behind a vertical dpc between the leaves, this dpc should be extended to cover the joint between any framing or sheathing and the wall. Pre-compressed foam sealing tapes may be preferred rather than dpcs or gunned mastic in these locations, because they maintain good contact over uneven surfaces and will continue to expand to fill any gaps even if there is shrinkage or movement at the interface between the wall and any timber component. Whatever junction is made between battens and the abutting wall it is important that there is at least an 8–10 mm gap between the ends or sides of the boards and any other wall material. This gap is intended to allow ventilation to the end grain of horizontal boards and the gap should not be filled with mastic, or any other sealant.

Figure 5.27 Board on board cladding 'oversailing' brickwork below

Junctions with other materials frequently involve the use of metal flashings either lead, galvanised or powder coated steel, or anodised or powder coated aluminium. Lead may be suitable for flashings below timber cladding if it can be dressed over and supported by a solid base, or around openings where it can be dressed back behind the boarding. It is not generally suitable however as a capping over the boards because if it is dressed down over and directly supported by the boards it will tend to block ventilation to the cavity. A possible exception is with open-jointed boards where adequate ventilation will occur through the joints.

It is important that the top edges of the boards, and particularly vertical boards, are protected from direct wetting. This can be best achieved by preformed metal flashings that can project out over the boards without the need for support.

A downstand leg 10 mm ahead of the cladding face will shed water clear of the top edge, but the further a flashing projects the more the shadow will prevent the wood below from bleaching, if this is the aim. Projecting the flashing further out will also not prevent rainwater being blown onto the face of the wall at some point below.

A particular condition that requires careful detailing is when a flashing over a window opening in vertical boarding needs to be extended over the adjoining boards. This requires the boards to be cut back to allow for the horizontal extension of the flashing. This is difficult with flush boards, but more easily worked out with a board-on-board layout.

At the base of any wood cladding it is important to ensure that at least a 15 mm gap is left between the underside of the boards and the top of the flashing. This is to allow drainage of moisture from the cavity and to provide sufficient ventilation. With vertical boarding in particular, it will also avoid any absorption of moisture into the end grain of the boards.

A flashing at the base of the cladding should extend back for the full depth of the cavity and be dressed up against the vertical face of the wall. If there is a breather membrane at the back, this should be dressed down over the upstand leg, and it is preferable if the flashing is pitched to the outside to avoid any water gathering on the top surface. If a base flashing needs to project some distance to oversail a wall below, the projection should be at a sufficiently steep pitch that it prevents water splashing off the surface of the metal and wetting the bottom of the boards. Otherwise this can lead to excessive wetting and consequent discolouration of the wood.

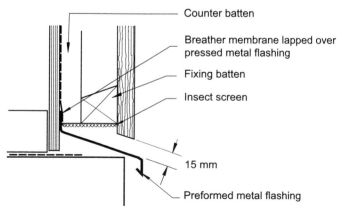

Counter batten

Breather membrane lapped over pressed metal flashing

Fixing batten

Insect screen

15 mm

Preformed metal flashing

Figure 5.28 Vertical boards over flashing

Figure 5.29 Detail at base of vertical cladding with metal flashing over concrete plinth

Concern is often expressed about the suitability of various metals to be used as flashings in conjunction with timber cladding. This is often due to reservations expressed by the suppliers of metal roofs such as lead, copper, aluminium, or galvanised steel, and generally concerns the extractives from wood causing possible deterioration of the metals.

Certainly, where some metal roofs have been in continuous direct contact with 'wet' wood, particularly those woods with a high tannin content, there have been cases of pitting and deterioration. However, in the case of cladding flashings, the wetting will be intermittent, and drying out will always occur between, nor will the wood be in direct contact with the flashing. Certainly run-off of any tannin during the initial bleaching process, may build up as a brown coating on the surface of the metal, but this can be cleaned off and, even if left, will not attack any metals other than exposed mild steel. Galvanising or powder coating should provide sufficient protection to mild steel, but cut ends or drilled holes may require extra protection. Using woods with a high tannin content, such as oak in a 'green' state, will mean a considerable run-off of tannin for an extended period. In this case it may be worth covering metal flashings at the base of the cladding with a strip of self-adhesive film that can be removed after the bleaching process is complete. This would largely eliminate the need for cleaning of the metal, but obviously care must be taken to choose a film that will not affect the coating when removed. A traditional alternative is to coat the metal with bituminous paint, but the appearance may not be visually acceptable.

5.7.4 Openings

Most areas of timber cladding will either contain openings for windows or doors, or be contained within a dimensional framework determined by areas of glazing or a strip of windows. Ideally any openings should be in multiples of the chosen board width to avoid the need to notch or split boards.

Having to notch or cut boards around openings is difficult to do and can lead to poor appearance. A dimensional relationship is particularly important between openings and board widths for board-on-board cladding otherwise the pattern of boarding may not relate either side of an opening. If the sizes and locations of openings are already determined, it may be necessary to choose a size of board, or vary the amount of overlap, specifically to relate to the predetermined dimensions of the openings. It is also important to consider the three dimensional relationship of flashings, sills and dpcs around any openings formed in the timber cladding to ensure that water is drained away to the outside of the wall. This is particularly true of vertical boarding where cut ends may be exposed directly to rainfall. Where fixings, such as screws and washers on green oak boards are very visible, care is necessary to ensure that there is a coherent pattern around openings.

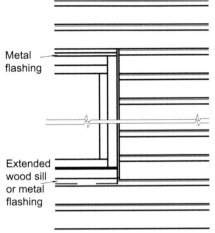

Metal flashing

Extended wood sill or metal flashing

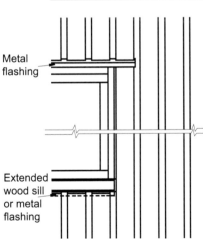

Metal flashing

Extended wood sill or metal flashing

Figure 5.30 Typical elevation details of windows in horizontal boarding and vertical board-on-board cladding

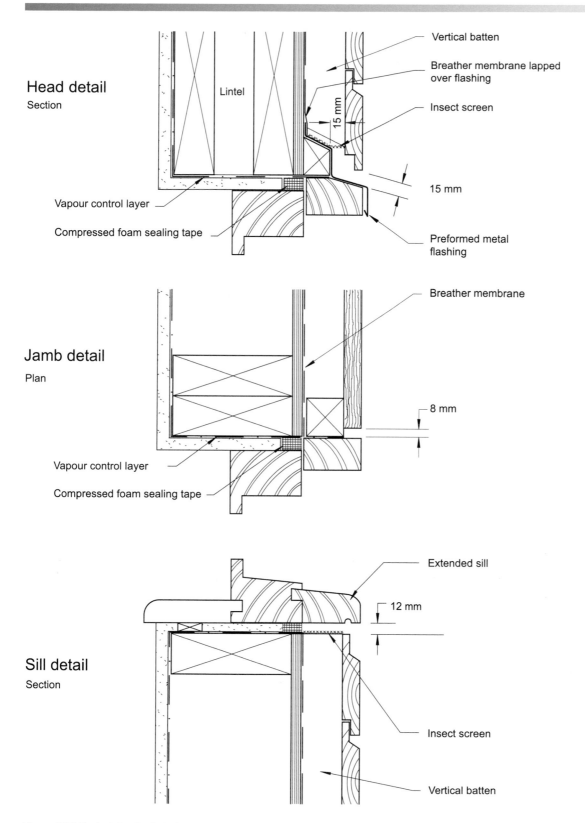

Head detail

Section

Lintel

15 mm

Vertical batten

Breather membrane lapped over flashing

Insect screen

15 mm

Preformed metal flashing

Vapour control layer

Compressed foam sealing tape

Jamb detail

Plan

Breather membrane

8 mm

Vapour control layer

Compressed foam sealing tape

Sill detail

Section

Extended sill

12 mm

Insect screen

Vertical batten

Figure 5.31 Typical detail of window in horizontal boarding
Note: A timber frame wall is shown: the detailing of the cladding with other forms of wall construction will be similar

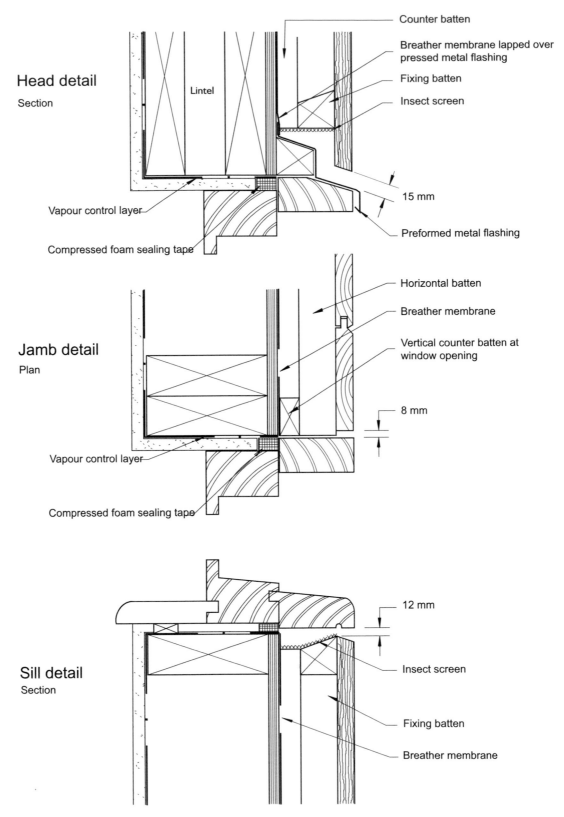

Head detail

Section

Lintel

Counter batten

Breather membrane lapped over pressed metal flashing

Fixing batten

Insect screen

15 mm

Preformed metal flashing

Vapour control layer

Compressed foam sealing tape

Jamb detail

Plan

Horizontal batten

Breather membrane

Vertical counter batten at window opening

8 mm

Vapour control layer

Compressed foam sealing tape

Sill detail

Section

12 mm

Insect screen

Fixing batten

Breather membrane

Figure 5.32 Typical detail of window in timber frame with vertical tongued and grooved boarding

Note: A timber frame wall is shown: the detailing of the cladding with other forms of wall construction will be similar

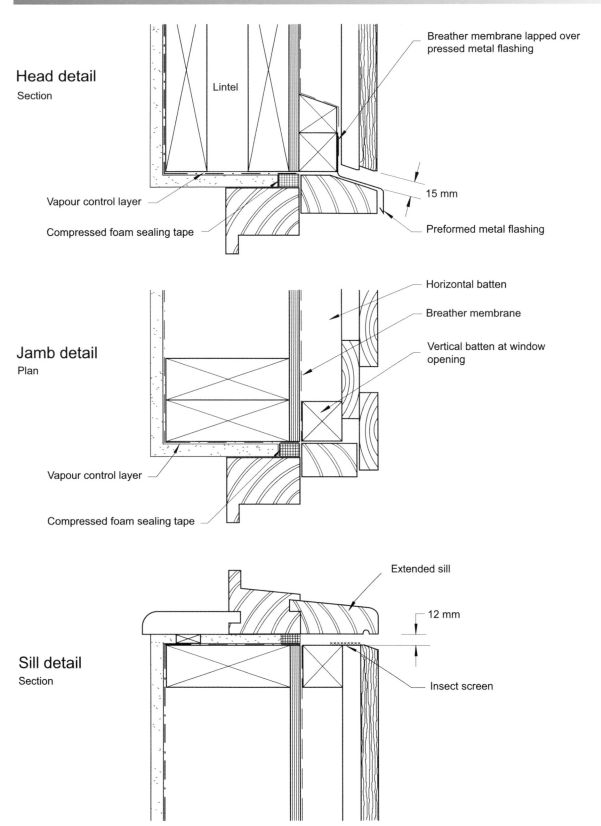

Head detail
Section

Lintel

Breather membrane lapped over pressed metal flashing

15 mm

Preformed metal flashing

Vapour control layer

Compressed foam sealing tape

Jamb detail
Plan

Horizontal batten

Breather membrane

Vertical batten at window opening

Vapour control layer

Compressed foam sealing tape

Sill detail
Section

Extended sill

12 mm

Insect screen

Figure 5.33 Typical detail of window in timber with vertical board-on-board cladding
Note: A timber frame wall is shown: the detailing of the cladding with other forms of wall construction will be similar

5.7.5 Corners

The detailing of both external and internal corners in timber cladding will have a strong visual impact, and should be related to other features such as the detailing of the cladding around window openings. In horizontal cladding, whether overlapped or flush, window openings were traditionally surrounded with an architrave section which covered the cut ends of the boards and also the edges of window frames. Corners were therefore treated in a similar way, with cover boards over the ends of the boards. It is now more common to stop the boards short of a fully expressed window frame, creating a shadow gap all round. This requires a high standard of work-manship in cutting horizontal boards. The window frames are then usually carried forward flush with the face of the boards. Transferring this principle to the corner, means that a solid corner piece is required flush with the outer face of the boards in the same relationship as the window framing. This can be achieved either with a solid square section, or by forming an L-shaped corner. An L-shape is sometimes reversed and corner packer omitted to create a re-entrant corner.

Figure 5.34 Solid timber corner detail, Henley River and Rowing Museum David Chipperfield Architects

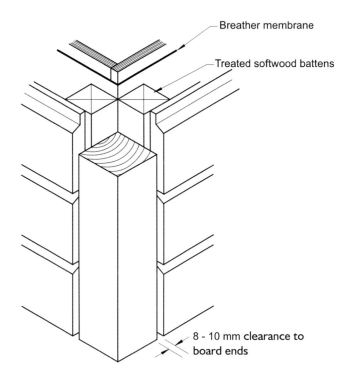

Breather membrane

Treated softwood battens

8 - 10 mm clearance to board ends

Figure 5.35 Solid timber corner detail in horizontal boarding

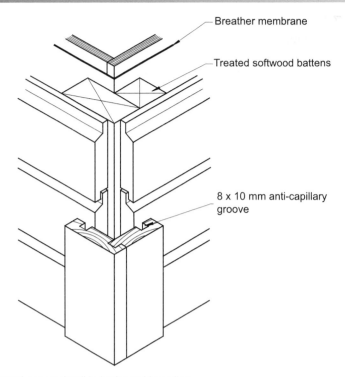

Breather membrane

Treated softwood battens

8 x 10 mm anti-capillary groove

Figure 5.36 Covered corner detail in horizontal boarding

Figure 5.37 Covered corner detail in horizontal boarding

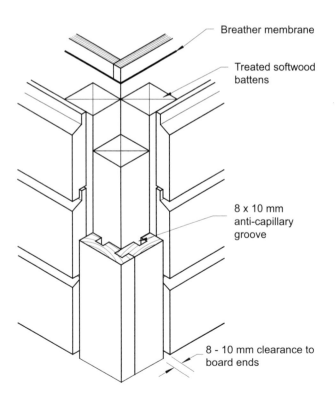

Breather membrane

Treated softwood battens

8 x 10 mm anti-capillary groove

8 - 10 mm clearance to board ends

Figure 5.38 Solid corner detail in horizontal boarding with preformed capping pieces

Figure 5.39 Solid corner detail with preformed capping pieces, National Maritime Museum, Falmouth
Architects: Long and Kentish
Photo © Long and Kentish

Figure 5.40 Re-entrant corner in horizontal boarding, National Botanic Garden of Wales
Architect: Foster and Partners
Photo: P Hislop

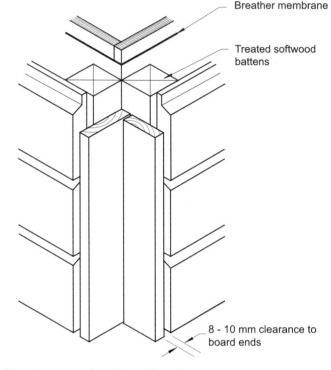

Figure 5.41 Re-entrant corner in horizontal boarding

Mitreing the ends of horizontal boards to meet on a corner is not recommended because, however tight the joint between board is initially, the natural tendency of wood to move, however slightly, will mean that the abutting surfaces will not remain flush to each other. Moisture pick-up in the end grain of the boards will cause them to swell and move apart. Any surface coating is likely to fail at this point because of this movement. Unfinished open-jointed boards have been used in a mitred form, but a gap has been left between the ends of the boards similar in size to the horizontal gap between boards and this conceals any variation between the faces.

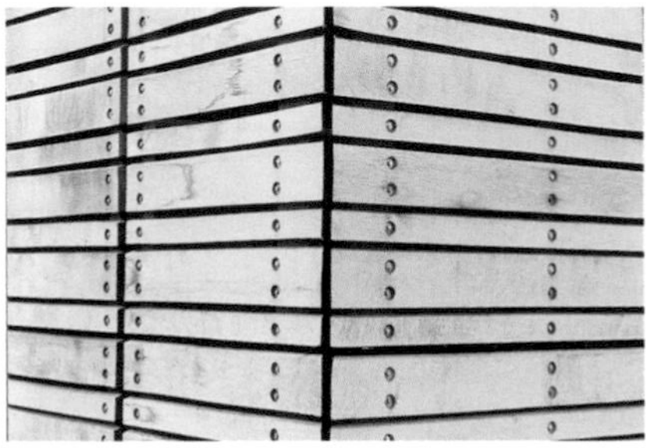

Figure 5.42 Open mitred corner in green oak boarding, Earth Centre, South Yorkshire
Architects: Feilden Clegg Bradley
Photo P Hislop

Both internal and external corners are more easily detailed with vertical boards, whether flush jointed or board-on-board. In either case a right angled corner can be made up by tonguing together two sections related in size to the dimensions of the boards on each elevation. Additional battens will be necessary behind these corner pieces and if there is a breather membrane this should be wrapped around the corner behind the battens.

Corner detailing for diagonal boards can be treated in a similar fashion to horizontal boards, but if the ends of the boards are exposed very careful cutting is required. Because of the quantity of water discharged by the joints from diagonal boards, the gap between the board ends and any vertical member should be increased to a minimum of 12 mm, and should be well sealed behind.

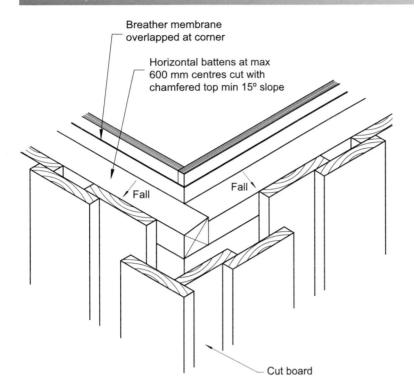

Breather membrane overlapped at corner

Horizontal battens at max 600 mm centres cut with chamfered top min 15° slope

Fall

Fall

Cut board

Figure 5.43 Typical corner detail in vertical board-on-board cladding

Figure 5.44 Corner detail, Seton Mains House
Paterson Architects
Photo © Keith Hunter Photography

6 Storage and installation

The overall performance and appearance of timber cladding of any sort will largely depend on how well it is stored and installed. The quality defined by careful specification and detail drawings may well be compromised by poor workmanship or on-site damage to materials in storage or during or after installation.

6.1 Storage

All timber components can suffer prior to erection from excessive exposure to wetting or construction dirt in storage. All stacks of boarding or panels should be protected from direct wetting by covers that still allow air circulation around the stacks. They should also be placed on battens, out of contact with soil or water on a level base, preferably a dry concrete slab. Batten spacing must be close enough to prevent deflection of the stack or individiual boards between supports. Edges of boards, particularly with profiles such as tongue and groove, need to be protected, and not damaged by overtight banding etc.

Where 'green' timber is specified for use, it may be worth stacking with sticks between layers of boards to allow sufficient air circulation to reduce the moisture content before erection. Typical board thicknesses will dry down quite quickly in reasonably dry weather, although this process will be quicker with softwoods than hardwoods. It is important to ensure that the sticks are clean and dry before use to help to avoid stick marking.

Particular care in storage and handling is necessary when the boards or panels are fully finished in order to avoid damage to the finish. 'Touching-up' is not recommended because of the difficulty of color matching and also achieving the same durability with site application of a finish.

However, it may be even more important to protect components such as boards or panels that are to be left unfinished, because soiling or marking, such as bootmarks, may be difficult to remove, particularly from sawn finishes where sanding would not be feasible. Left exposed on the visible face of the boards, such marks would take a considerable length of time for natural weathering to remove them.

6.2 Installation

The moisture content of boards should be checked and recorded immediately before installation as the moisture content may have changed since delivery. The actual moisture content of the wood at this stage should be within the range specified.

Where symmetrically profiled boards are to be used, and the growth rings are visible across the cross section of the board, the 'heartside' of the board should be to the outer face. The only exception is the inner layer of boards in a 'board-on-board' pattern, when the 'heartside' of the board should be to the inside (see Section 5.2 and *Figure 5.4*). This takes into account the likely distortion of the wood due to any variation in moisture content. Occasionally, stresses built up in kiln dried wood which is later resawn, can result in the natural tendency to change shape being reversed, and some distortion may have occurred in the opposite direction even before the boards are installed. If this occurs, it may be necessary to reconsider which way round the boards should be fixed to the building.

With all interlocking boards, whether overlapping or tongue and groove, a minimum 2 mm clearance should be left for possible expansion between parts of a board ie the tongue and groove, or any rebated sections (*Figures 5.15, 5.17*). This is for a maximum board width of about 150 mm; if the board is wider a larger clearance should be provided.

If the wood is to be used 'green', shrinkage rather than expansion of the board is more likely, and less clearance need be provided. However, because of this shrinkage, joints will open and sufficient overlap should be provided between boards to accommodate this. (Tongue and groove joints are not suitable for use with 'green' wood.) In an open-joint application the boards should be fixed so that the specified joint width is achieved after the initial drying shrinkage has taken place. It may be necessary to determine the gap to be provided at installation by checking the actual moisture content of the timber, and calculating the amount of drying shrinkage to be expected.

Where board lengths are to be butt jointed, it is recommended to provide at least a 5 mm gap for ventilation and drainage on unfinished wood, but this may not be sufficient to allow insertion of a brush to re-coat the ends of the boards when maintenance is required. If visually acceptable, an 8 mm gap is the usual minimum space for this.

Boards must always be butt jointed over battens, whether vertical or horizontal. But single battens are not usually wide enough to allow both board ends to be fixed. If the boarding is 'panellised' and the boards are all of the same length, double battens can be used. Where boards are random lengths they must still be in multiples of the batten spacing, but short lengths of the standard size battens can be nailed to the side or top of the main battens to provide additional space for fixing the end of one of the boards. The length of this addditional piece of batten should be at least three times the face width of the boards (*Figure 5.6*).

An alternative on thicker boards or narrow profiled sections, is to form a lap joint by rebating the ends of the section to allow an overlap which can be fixed together to the standard support batten with a single nail or screw. However, this requires considerable precise preparation and should be limited to hardwood cladding profiles.

The finished widths of boards will be less than the nominal, or basic, size ie the finished size of a nominal 150 mm board will be about 144 mm due to cutting and planing. If the overall layout of the cladding is dimensioned on the basis of multiples of the nominal size, it will be necessary to adjust the gap between boards to allow for the reduction in the finished size of the board during fixing. This is to ensure that the boarding conforms with the overall dimensions required, and also coincides with such features as window openings (horizontally or vertically).

If boards are to be left unfinished, nails or screws (unless they are designed to be recessed) should be driven to lie as flush as possible with the surface of the wood after initial drying has taken place.

If a surface coating system is to be applied, the nails or screws should be slightly recessed to allow for a slight build up of the coating over the head.

If surface coating systems are to be added on site, at least the first coat should be applied to all faces of the boards before they are installed. In particular coatings should be applied thickly to any exposed end grain. Pre-coating will even out moisture absorption on all faces, reducing the risk of distortion across the section. It also avoids the risk of uncoated surfaces appearing on the face of the cladding due to shrinkage which can occur if all coats are only applied after installation (*Figure 3.3*).

Removing sharp arrises by sanding or chamfering will extend the life of surface coatings, particularly on horizontal boards. This is because liquid coatings will tend to pull away from sharp edges due to surface tension, resulting in a reduced film thickness at the most critical points, where any erosion from water run-off will be most severe.

7 Maintenance

With unfinished boards, shingles or shakes, little maintenance should be required although, depending on the level of pollution of the environment or proximity of foliage etc, the surface may require cleaning at some point. There are a number of commercial cleaning products available that will remove surface staining, and to some extent the bleached surface of the wood. They will also remove, within some limits, any iron staining that may have occurred in woods with a high tannin content. If the source of the staining or soiling, eg pollution from traffic, is likely to remain, it may be advisable to use one of the surface coatings recommended by the manufacturers of the cleaning solution after the cleaning process has been completed. These are colourless liquids and basically reduce the moisture absorption of the wood. However, because they are clear they have little resistance to ultraviolet light and may require re-application fairly frequently.

Some discolouration of wood may be entirely due to excessive moisture pick-up from localised wetting such as rainwater run-off. Such areas may also benefit from application of the clear penetrating liquids that reduce moisture pick-up. These should only be applied to dry surfaces after any staining has been cleaned off. Because they are clear they are not visible and might be applied to areas where, for instance regular splashback is occurring leading to excessive wetting. However, they should be tested in small areas before they are applied generally to ensure that they will not appear too different to any surface left untreated. They will also require re-application, possibly at 2–3 years frequency or less, on faces exposed to full sun.

All coated timber cladding will at some point require re-coating. The frequency will depend on a number of factors, such as the way the finish has been applied initially or to the degree of exposure on site. Factory-applied finishes applicable to various panel products, and to a lesser extent, on pre-finished board profiles, will probably outlast any site-applied coating, simply because the process is tightly controlled, including the moisture content of the wood, the limited exposure to ultraviolet light before application, the cleanliness of the environment, and the standard of workmanship.

These factory finishes will last many years without need for maintenance and may be guaranteed to achieve a particular life, but may require specialist treatment when they eventually need replacing, and the manufacturer of the component or coating should be consulted. Where coatings are applied on site the quality is less controlled and inevitably their life will be dependent on the variables involved.

With the rapid technical developments occurring in preservation and paint technology it is of prime importance prior to any maintenance that the materials used for various functions are compatible with each other. For instance, water-based coating systems are now replacing spirit based, and chemical preservative use is also changing. The performance of flame retardant treatments may also be affected by any coatings applied.

For these reasons information on the types of treatment or coating system used initially must be supplied to those responsible for the maintenance of any building. This will allow them to check with manufacturers whether

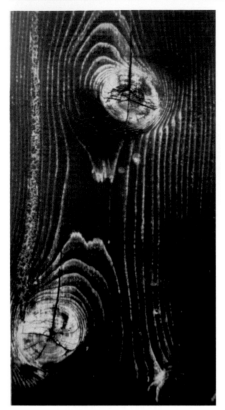

Figure 7.1 Stain finish eroded beyond the point at which re-coating should take place

materials proposed for maintenance will be compatible with coatings or other treatments originally applied. It is particularly important for instance that film-forming surface coatings are not used over original vapour permeable coatings as this may compromise the breathability of the original finish.

Even if the original finishing system is to be re-applied, it is essential to know from the manufacturers what preparation may be necessary prior to re-coating. This level of preparation will depend largely on the level of deterioration of the original finish that has occurred. If, for instance, a stain finish has deteriorated to the extent that areas of bleached wood are visible, it will be necessary to take the surface back to clean wood before re-coating, whereas if the surface has merely faded or suffered some surface erosion, it may only be necessary to brush off loose particles before re-coating.

Wood cladding may have been designed to be left to bleach naturally without any finish, but at some stage the building owner may decide that he would prefer a coloured appearance. In this case the bleached surface of the wood must be removed back to clear wood before anything is applied, otherwise the coating will not obtain sufficient adhesion to the wood, and re-coating will be necessary at frequent intervals. Whether a coating is applied initially or added at a later date it is important that the client understands that the surface must not be allowed to deteriorate to the extent that a great deal of preparatory work would be required before a new coat can be applied.

If it is intended to add a coating to hardwood cladding that was originally left unfinished it is important that coating manufacturers should be consulted before any product is specified because hardwoods vary considerably in their suitability for coatings.

The client should understand that the life of any coating system will depend on the degree of exposure to sun and weather. However, a detailed survey of the elevations of a building prior to any maintenance programme could indicate that maintenance may only be necessary on the more exposed parts. In this case re-coating could be limited to those areas where deterioration was noted providing this did not result in an unacceptable discrepancy in colour. This might considerably reduce the cost of maintenance in materials, labour, and possibly the need for scaffolding.

After any maintenance regime, information should again be provided to the client on the materials and processes used for future reference.

References

Standards

BS 1186-3: 1990 Timber for and workmanship in joinery. Specification for wood trim and its fixing.

BS 8417: 2003 Preservation of timber. Recommendations.

BS EN 314-2: 1993 Plywood. Bonding quality. Requirements.

BS EN 350-1: 1994 Durability of wood and wood-based products. Natural durability of solid wood. Guide to the principles of testing and classification of natural durability of wood.

BS EN 350-2: 1994 Durability of wood and wood-based products. Natural durability of solid wood. Guide to natural durability and treatability of selected wood species of importance in Europe.

BS EN 14915: 2006 Solid wood panelling and cladding. Characteristics, evaluation of conformity and marking.

BS EN 15146: 2006 Solid softwood panelling and cladding. Machined profiles without tongue and groove.

TRADA Technology publications
Wood Information Sheets
available as printed copies or to download from
www.trada.co.uk/bookshop

Durability by design. WIS 4 – 28. Revised 2004.

Exterior coatings on 'alternative' hardwoods. WIS 2/3 – 54. 2000.

Flame retardant treatments for timber. WIS 2/3 – 3. Revised 2003.

Finishes for external timber. WIS 2/3 – 1. Revised 2005.

Introducing wood. WIS 2/3 – 28. Revised 2003.

Moisture in timber. WIS 4 – 14. Revised 2006.

Preservative treatment for timber: a guide to specification. WIS 2/3 – 16. Revised 2006.

Timbers their properties and uses. WIS 2/3 – 10. Revised 2002.

Wood decorative and practical. WIS 2/3 – 6. Revised 1999.

Wood preservation: chemicals and processes. WIS 2/3 – 33. Revised 2005.

Wood Protection Association

available to download from www.wood-protection.org or from www.trada.co.uk

Industrial wood preservation – Specification and practice. Edition 1/2007.

Industrial flame retardant treatment of solid timber and panel products. Edition 2/ 2007.

Other information websites:

BM TRADA Certification www.bmtrada.co.uk

Canadian Standards Association (CSA) www.csa.ca

Central Point of Expertise on Timber (CPET) www.proforest.net/cpet

Forest Stewardship Council (FSC) www.fsc.org

Malaysian Timber Certification Council www.mtcc.com.my

Programme for the Endorsement of Forest Certification schemes (PEFC) www.pefc.org

Sustainable Forestry Initiative (SFI) (USA) www.aboutsfi.org

TRADA and TRADA Technology www.trada.co.uk

Appendix I Softwoods commonly used for cladding

European redwood (*Pinus sylvestris*)

This is largely imported from a number of European countries, including Scandinavia, Russia and Latvia although now also available in some quantity from UK sources where it is referred to as Scots pine. For joinery purposes the imported wood is preferred because of its slow growth and consequent strength. This is less important for cladding and home-grown wood is quite suitable, although may need more selection to reach the necessary classification under *BS 1186-3*. It is defined as a medium movement wood. It is rated as Class 4, slightly durable and should be impregnated with preservative when used for cladding and can be readily treated. It tends to have a high proportion of large and loose knots and is also quite resinous. It is normally finished with an opaque or translucent coating but there is a risk of resin exudation, particularly if dark colours are used on walls exposed to the sun because of the increased surface temperature.

European redwood is also available modified by heat or chemical treatment to achieve adequate durability for cladding without the use of preservatives.

European redwood
Note: the photograph shows freshly planed, unfinished timber

European whitewood (*Picea abies*)

Also largely imported from Europe (including Scandinavia, Russia and Latvia), although now available in some quantity from UK sources of sufficient quality for cladding use where it is usually referred to as spruce.

It is less strong than redwood but has adequate strength for cladding boards. It is referred to as medium movement wood. It is rated as Class 4, slightly durable and should be impregnated with preservative, although it is more difficult to treat than European redwood.

This wood has been traditionally used for timber cladding in Scandinavia because it is non-resinous and generally has smaller knots than redwood. It is also more moisture resistant than European redwood, but is normally finished with an opaque or translucent coating.

European whitewood is also available modified by heat or chemical treatment to achieve adequate durability without the use of preservatives.

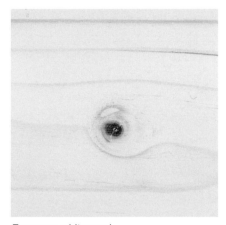

European whitewood
Note: the photograph shows freshly planed, unfinished timber

European larch (*Larix decidua*)

This has long been used for cladding in Europe, but until recently, was rarely been used for this purpose in the UK. Although often imported from Scandinavia, a considerable quantity is now available from UK plantations. European larch from Siberia or Alpine areas has the advantage of being very slow grown and is consequently denser, straight grained and less knotty.

It is a very strong robust wood, and good quality timber can be relatively knot free although some knots can be "loose". It varies considerably in quality and needs careful selection. Better quality wood was traditionally used for boat building and the poorer for fencing. It is referred to as

European larch
Note: the photograph shows freshly planed, unfinished timber

a small movement wood. It is rated as Class 3, moderately durable and if the sapwood is excluded can be used untreated for cladding. The wood can be left unfinished, but if sapwood is not excluded the wood requires treatment.

Note: Japanese larch (*Larix kaempferi*) and some of the hybrid species are not recommended for use as cladding without preservative treatment.

Douglas fir (*Pseudotsuga menziesii*)

Traditionally imported from North America (sometimes confusingly referred to as Oregon Pine or British Columbian Pine) the wood is now also available home-grown. It is a straight grained strong, robust wood, available in large sections and long lengths. It has a quite high tannin content and is resinous, although home grown is less resinous than imported. It is referred to as a small movement wood. Imported material is rated as Class 3, moderately durable but home-grown wood is less durable and is rated as Class 3–4 moderately–slightly durable).

Imported wood can be used untreated for cladding if sapwood is excluded, but it may be necessary to treat home-grown wood, in which case the sapwood need not be removed, but the wood is somewhat resistant to treatment. The wood can be left unfinished to bleach.

Western red cedar (*Thuja plicata*)

Although the majority of this wood is imported from North America, it is also now available home-grown. The imported wood is available in large sections and long lengths from Canada and the US West Coast. Because of its inherent durability it is the most popular wood for cladding, but is becoming increasingly expensive. It is straight grained and largely free of knots, although small knots are more frequent in home-grown wood. It is a relatively soft, brittle wood that can be easily dented or scraped, so may not be the best choice if used at low level and exposed to the risk of mechanical damage.

It is referred to as a small movement wood. It is rated as Class 2, durable and can therefore be used untreated if the sapwood is excluded. *BS 8417* gives a 60 year service life for the untreated wood if sapwood is excluded. It is resistant to preservative treatment.

It has a high tannin content which can be corrosive to iron, and can itself stain badly as a result of any corrosion. It can be left unfinished and will bleach to a particularly attractive lustrous silver-grey. Because the surface is open-textured it is not advisable to use it unfinished in locations where there is a high level of pollution from traffic or industrial processing.

Douglas fir
Note: the photograph shows freshly planed, unfinished timber

Western red cedar
Note: the photograph shows freshly planed, unfinished timber

Appendix 2 Hardwoods used for cladding

Temperate species
Of the many temperate hardwoods available only the following have been included because of the natural durability of their heartwood.

European oak (*Quercus robur*)
This is now readily available, either home-grown or imported from Europe, in particular France, Germany and Eastern Europe. It is rated as a durable timber of medium movement. It is often specified to be used green (undried), which saves the cost of kilning, but care must be taken in designing the fixings in this case as considerable shrinkage in thickness and board width will occur after erection. Used green, the wood is relatively malleable and can be held back flat by screw fixings to the sub-structure. Once dry, the wood becomes extremely hard and resistant to mechanical damage.

As a considerable amount of tannin will exude from the wood particularly from green wood during the initial weathering and bleaching, stainless steel, or other non-ferrous fixings, should always be used.

Like most hardwoods, it is difficult to achieve good adhesion with coatings and most oak cladding has traditionally been left unfinished to bleach to grey.

Even limiting board widths to 150 mm maximum, it is not easy to obtain oak to Class 1 quality under *BS 1186-3* and Class 2 would be more typical. Lengths of board, particularly if from a home-grown source should preferably be limited to about 2.4 m maximum although some longer lengths may be available from some suppliers. The wood, whether home grown or imported from Europe is available certified under FSC or PEFC schemes.

European / American white oak
Note: the photograph shows freshly planed, unfinished timber

American white oak (*Quercus alba*)
Although this has most of the characteristics of European oak, it is imported from North America kiln dried to a very low moisture content. This makes it suitable for internal joinery, but can lead to problems externally unless the wood is conditioned to a suitable moisture content. There is a risk of extensive shakes occurring in the surface of the wood, even after conditioning. The timber from North America is available certified under the PEFC system.

Sweet chestnut (*Castanea sativa*)
This timber is available home grown in some parts of the UK in relatively small quantities. It is similar to European oak in its properties with the same level of tannin exudation, but is rated as a small movement timber. Available lengths and sizes are similar to European oak and the same care is required if it is used green. Home-grown timber is generally available certified under the FSC system by the Forestry Commission.

Sweet chestnut
Note: the photograph shows freshly planed, unfinished timber

Tropical hardwoods

Tropical hardwoods suitable for cladding are generally rated as either durable or very durable. Some of the tropical hardwoods traditionally used for cladding, particularly those from Africa and the Far East have not been available with full certification of sustainable management. However, the situation is changing in that some timbers, such as teak and iroko are now available certified if they are plantation grown, or can satisfy the rules of sustainable management.

There are also a number of less well known, secondary species, many from Central and South America with full FSC certification, which are now being imported into the UK. They are rated as durable or very durable and are dense or very dense timbers. Moisture movement is either small or medium. Some of the timbers will darken initially on exposure, but in the long term, without a surface coating, they will all bleach to a similar grey colour.

Timbers that have been used for cladding include:

- Angelim
- Cumaru
- Louro
- Itauba
- Jatoba
- Kauri
- Massaranduba
- Purpleheart
- Tatajuba

Some of these may be offered as sub species and the importers should be approached for detailed performance characteristics and for information on availability, lengths and sizes.

Appendix 3 Specification checklist

This checklist is intended to act as an *aide-mémoire* but may not necessarily cover every aspect that may be required in specifying timber cladding for any particular project.

Timber

Characteristics	Notes
Durability	Class 3, Moderately durable, or better (*BS EN 352-2*), or specify preservative treatment. Exclude sapwood in timbers without preservative pre-treatment.
Movement characteristics	Small or medium movement timbers preferable.
Quality	Specify to *BS 1186-3* Class 1, 2 or 3 or Specifiy to *BS EN 15146*—Species grades A and B or Obtain and approve samples and/or cladding mock-up
Moisture content	Kiln or air dried: 16% +/- 2%. Green timber (ie undried): over 20%.
Tannin content	Timbers with high tannin content may require special consideration in building design and detailing eg non-ferrous fixings. Consider effect of tannin run-off on other materials.
Strength, impact resistance	Consider risk of mechanical damage, vandalism etc - choice of more impact-resistant species.

Treatments and finishes	Notes
Preservative pre-treatment	Preferably applied by pressure/vacuum treatments or (less effective) immersion. Cut ends of treated timber on site should be liberally treated with compatible preservative. Water-borne copper organics can be used with or without surface coatings. Organic solvents need surface coatings. Micro-emulsions need surface coatings. Boron salts need surface coatings.
Heat treated modified timber **Chemically modified timber**	Proprietary products; refer to manufacturers details.
Surface coatings	Microporous paints or stains, applied in accordance with manufacturers instructions. Pigmented coatings necessary to resist uv degradation. Factory application preferable. On site application: at least one coat to be applied to all faces before installation.
Flame retardant treatment	Vacuum/pressure treatment necessary, not surface coating. Choice of treatment dependent on whether timber is to be coated. Effectiveness depends upon species: check with treatment manufacturer.

Fixings and ancillaries	Notes
Timber battens	Normally treated softwood; 2.5 x board thickness with standard nails; 2 x board thickness with ring-shank nails. Typically 38 x 38 mm, 600 mm max centres (should be reduced if cladding is to be used green).
Nails	Typically used for softwood boards. Austenitic stainless steel recommended, even if wood is to be coated; essential for all species left unfinished and for all high tannin timbers.
Screws and washers	Typically used for hardwood boards in pre-drilled oversize holes. Additional stainless steel washers may be required if wood is to be used green. Austenitic stainless steel recommended, even if wood is to be coated; essential for all species left unfinished and for all high tannin timbers.
Clips	Austenitic stainless steel. Purpose-made product—discuss with manufacturer.
Cavity barriers	Treated timber or proprietary products; should not inhibit cavity ventilation and drainage. Check acceptability of design solution with building control.
Insect mesh	Proprietary products—see manufacturer's details.

Detail design

Board orientation and profiles	Notes
Horizontal boarding; preferably not exceeding 150 mm face width	Open joint chamfered boards; 8–15 mm gap between boards at outer face. (Breather membranes at risk of uv attack if gaps above 10 mm).
	Square edge; vertical overlaps min 25 mm.
	Feather edge; vertical overlaps min 25 mm.
	Rebated feather edge; vertical overlaps min 15 mm; 2 mm gap between rebate and board below.
	Shiplap; vertical overlaps min 15 mm; 2 mm gap between rebate and upstand.
Horizontal boarding; preferably not exceeding 125 mm face width	Tongued and grooved; min 10 mm tongue; 2 mm gap between tongue and groove and shoulders.
	Install tongue up.
	Secret nailing not recommended unless rebated tongued and grooved profile.
Diagonal boarding	Rebated overlapping preferred profile; max 150 mm face width. 20 mm minimum overlap.
Vertical boarding; preferably not exceeding 125 mm face width	Tongued and grooved; min 12 mm groove; 2 mm gap between tongue and groove and shoulders.
Vertical boarding; preferably not exceeding 150 mm face width	Rebated overlapping; overlaps min 20 mm.
	Board on board; board widths can vary between inner and outer layer; overlaps 20–25 mm.
	Open joint: min 8–15 mm gap between boards at outer face. (Breather membranes at risk of uv attack).

Board lengths	Notes
Choice of species	Softwood; average lengths available 2.1–4.2 m (max 4.8 m).
	Temperate hardwood; average lengths 2.0–4.0 m (max 5 m).
	Tropical hardwood (varies with species); average lengths available 2.1–4.2 m (max 4.8 m).
Vertical boards	Preferable to limit lengths to storey heights; vertical end-to-end joints very visible in the long term. End joints must relate to batten positions.
Horizontal boards	Panellised; all end joints in line, simplifies fixing to battens but joint positions need to be carefully related to openings and overall dimensions. Simplifies prefabrication but may increase costs due to wastage.
	Monolithic: end joints related to batten positions but otherwise random.

Installation

Actions	Notes
Setting out	Ensure that boards are positioned 'on station' with regard to openings and overall dimensions.
Gaps between boards	Ensure sufficient clearance for possible expansion of 2 mm.
Clearance	Ensure 8–10 mm gap left between ends and sides of boards and other materials or wood trim.
End joints: horizontal boarding	With monolithic layouts ensure that short lengths of battens are added at end joint positions to provide fixing for board ends. Gap boards min 5 mm at end joints.
End joints: vertical boarding	With monolithic layouts ensure that short lengths of battens are added at end joint positions to provide fixing for board ends. At end joints of vertical boards chamfer top and bottom end of each board to ensure drainage. Gap boards min 5 mm at end joints.
Overlapping or board on board types	Ensure that fixings through outer board do not pass through board behind to avoid splitting.
Orientation of boards	With symmetrical boards check that heart side face is to outside. With board on board cladding the heart side face of the inner boards should face inwards and on the outer boards it should face out.
Fixings	Where boards are to be left unfinished do not overdrive nails. Nail heads should be flush with the face of the board. In green wood, position screws in oversize holes to allow maximum clearance as wood shrinks.
Coating	Apply minimum of prime coat and one finish coat to all faces of boards and two coats to exposed end grain at cut edges.